THE FIRST AND SECONI  S

of

AEROSPACE FUELS

A Personal View

Eric M Goodger

Autumn 2007

Published by
LANDFALL PRESS
© **LANDFALL PRESS**

ISBN 978-0-9520186-4-3

Printed and bound in England
Cover design and layout by GUY POLTOCK
*Acknowledgement is made gratefully
to many colleagues and friends
in the energy industry, Cranfield University,
QinetiQ, the Royal Aeronautical Society and the Energy Institute*

To the memory of

Kathleen R
(1920 - 1989)
&
Hilda L
(1923 - 2004)

"Fate managed twice to break his heart ....
.... but failed to break his spirit"

Particular acknowledgement is made to:

Catherine Cosgrove ⎞   of the
John Phipps ⎬ Energy Institute
Chris Baker ⎠   London
Brian Riddle of the Royal Aeronautical Society, London
Alisdair Clark of British Petroleum, Sunbury
Martin Malloy of UK Defence Standardization, Glasgow
Professor A C McIntosh of the University of Leeds
John R Jammes of Cranfield University

Dedicated to
CRANFIELD
(Crucible of Quality)

The First and Second Centuries of
Aerospace Fuels
A Personal View

The First and Second Centuries of
Aerospace Fuels
A Personal View

CONTENTS

The First and Second Centuries of Aerospace Fuels
by
Eric M Goodger

Executive Summary

The first century of controllable powered flight is considered to have dawned in 1903, courtesy of the Wright Brothers, one of the precursors being the emergence of the oil industry some 44 years earlier   Designs of aircraft, engines and their fuels developed apace, driven by the pressures of war and the demands for rapid travel.   The anti-knock qualities of aviation gasolines reached a peak in WW2, ultimately to combat the menace of the V-1 flying bomb which, operating on a modest-quality motor gasoline, demonstrated dramatically the superiority of jet propulsion over the conventional piston-engine/propeller combination.   This message was reinforced by the entry of the Meteor twin-jet aircraft into active service in Europe.

With the advent of the second century of fuelling aerospace vehicles, enhancement in overall efficiency continues, and interest in now focusing on topics such as:

- harnessing insect behaviour to assist altitude relight,

- improving control of oxidation,

- researching supplemental and substitute fuels (of which hydrogen appears to offer the optimal solution for both jet engines and fuel cells),

- increasing accuracy, speed and convenience of fuel property testing,

- developing pulsed detonation for practical devices,

- using ion and other advanced forms of propulsion (including antimatter) for deep space exploration, plus

- exerting closer control over emissions of carbon dioxide, and of water in contrails.

This project is not a comprehensive treatise on the subject of aerospace fuels: this has been handled elsewhere.   Rather it is a record (extended blog?) of those developments that have struck the writer (almost literally during WW2!) as his career progressed within the ambience of the subject as a whole.

Regarding presentation style, our aim has been to minimise large areas of unbroken text, to use bullet points and similar devices to present concise nuggets of information in digestible portions - supported by evocative artwork - and to employ some quirkiness here and there, with even a spot of humour despite the serious nature of the subject. We hope that the reader will gain as much pleasure in tackling this opus as we had in preparing it.

Special thanks are due to our Computer Graphics Artist, Guy Poltock, for both his detailed and overall contributions to the production of this work.

E M G
Landfall Press
November 2007

THE FIRST AND SECOND CENTURIES OF AEROSPACE FUELS

A PERSONAL VIEW

Without History, Citizenship has no root
Without Citizenship, History has no fruit

ANON

1. 1903 - ENTER THE FIRST CENTURY OF AEROSPACE

It is sometimes difficult to pinpoint the origin of a particular activity in history since the prevailing climate of opinion can obscure the actual birth. So it is with aviation because of early attempts at gliding and ballooning by luminaries such as Eilmer the Malmesbury monk, Cayley, Lilienthal, Stringfellow, Henson, the Montgolfiers, and many others including C Ader who is reputed to have flown for some 150 ft. under steam power in 1890. Nevertheless, the world's first manned, sustained, controlled, powered flight in a heavier-than-air machine is recognised as that by the Wright cycle makers, Wilbur and Orville, at Kitty Hawk, North Carolina, in their Flyer aircraft, fitted with a 4-cylinder gasoline engine developing 9 kW at 1025 rpm, on 17th December 1903. The first flight that day lasted for 12 seconds at a height of 10 ft over 120 ft., slightly less than the wingspan of the HP42 Hanno, but the fourth flight endured for 59 seconds while covering 852 ft.

However, this event became possible largely because another enterprise - the oil age - had emerged some 44 years earlier when, following the accidental discovery of oil in a coal mine at Riddings, Derbyshire, 'Colonel' Edwin Drake punctured the Earth's surface purposefully, and located oil at a depth of 69 ft at Titusville, Pennsylvania. A straight-run gasoline of anti-knock quality equivalent to about 38 octane number was therefore available for aviation to start drawing tentative breaths in its first century.

Aviation then literally 'took off', marked by enthusiasts piloting either replicas of the Flyer, or designs of their own, with mixed levels of success. It is recorded, for instance, that the Honourable Charles Stewart Rolls met his untimely end in a French-built Flyer in 1910. It seems remarkable that a mere 4 years had elapsed since the formation of the Rolls-Royce partnership which, despite this setback, led to the pinnacle of excellence it eventually achieved. The illustrious roll call of designers and/or pilots features Alcock & Brown, Bleriot, Cierva, Cobham, Cody, Fokker, Gaunt (also a cycle maker), Grahame-White, Handley Page, Hawker, Kingsford Smith, Lindbergh, Maxim, Miles, Mitchell, Moore-Brabazon, Mollison, Pilcher, Wilely Post, A V Roe, Scott & Black, Shorts, Ross and Keith Smith, and a host of others, including the ladies Jean Batten, Amelia Earhart, Amy Johnson and the Duchess of Bedford. Airfields then became established to support this new activity, highlighting names like Brooklands, Duxford, Mildenhall, Southport and Sheppey, together with those having personal connections like Biggin Hill, Croydon, Gatwick, Hendon, Henlow and Ramsgate.

This writer's youthful imagination was sparked by outstanding events such as the Schneider Trophy success, the global pathfinding by Imperial Airways, wings over Everest, sighting the stately R101 shortly before her demise in France, together with the debuts of the 'C' class flying boats, the 'Britain First' Blenheim, the legendary Spitfire and, latterly, the Comet airliner.

Figure 1

LIQUID PETROLEUM FUELS

Technical Name	General Name	Distillation Range °C	Typical Density kg/L @ 15°C	SIT °C
GASOLINE - Aviation (Avgas)	**Petrol**	**40-153**	**0.72**	**470**
- Motor (Mogas)	"	25-190	0.75	400
KEROSINE - Aviation (Avtur)	**Kerosene**	**150-260**	**0.80**	**255**
Gas Oil (DERV)	Diesel	165-350	0.84	247
Diesel Fuel	Heavy Diesel	200 + *	0.86	235
Residual Fuel Oil	Fuel Oil	*	0.95-0.97	?

SIT = minimum spontaneous ignition temperature

(Names in parentheses are UK Joint Services designations)

* Hydrocarbon molecules 'crack' above 370°C, hence heavy fuels cannot be fully distilled

But before attempting to chart the initial rise of the accompanying aviation fuel industry, it is prudent to address some nomenclature in order to avoid any confusions that may arise. The technical names in Fig. 1 are those agreed jointly by the Institute of Petroleum (now the Energy Institute) in UK, and the American Society for Testing & Materials in US. In particular, the difference in the spelling of Kerosine arose because the two aforementioned authorities adopted the 'i' spelling for **commercial blends**, and the 'e' spelling for **individual hydrocarbons** such as ethene, propene, benzene, toluene etc., etc.. Also in UK, the Joint Services Designation for petroleum fuels is shown in the concise terms of **Avgas, Mogas** and **Avtur**. It is noteworthy that these commercial petroleum fuel blends have been arranged here in ascending order of density - this is because this writer, during a lifetime of teaching the subject, has found it invaluable to use the modern expression of density (replacing the earlier specific gravity and relative density, although the numerical values are virtually identical) as a basis of identification and comparison. The temperature ranges of distillation ('cuts') are seen to rise in level with increase in density, indicating that the heavier fuels are less volatile, and spontaneous ignitability also rises.

2. Background to the Leaded Gasoline Saga

The following discussion outlines the background from which the fuel-lead saga evolved. The aftermath of Drake's well in 1859 was the replacement of coal tar by petroleum as a source of gasoline-type distillate fuels, as used in Otto's four-stroke piston engine and the emerging automotive industry. However, during the 1910s, the ruling in US was that gasoline was too flammable to be stored safely in residential properties, consequently the less volatile kerosine was explored as an alternative, but the problem of combustion roughness (eventually termed **spark knock**) became dramatically apparent in the form of cracked cylinder heads and pistons. The underlying cause was initially ascribed to pre-ignition, until the discovery that this phenomenon occurred at the end, rather than the beginning, of the combustion process.

Alternative theories regarding this critical property of a spark-ignited fuel centred firstly on volatility and then density, leading to the essential requirement for a rational explanation of the knock problem so that the mechanism could be understood and controlled. Nowadays, knock is generally accepted to arise from spontaneous ignition at many centres within the unburnt charge ahead of the advancing main flame within the chamber, when the operating conditions become more than usually severe by reason of higher levels of inlet pressure, temperature, compression ratio and/or spark advance (Fig. 2).

In essence, the fuel requirement to avoid spark knock is seen to be a low level of spontaneous ignitability, in terms of a high spontaneous ignition temperature, [In the diesel engine, on the other hand, the reverse is the case since a high level of spontaneous ignitability is essential to promote ignition, with minimal delay following injection in order to avoid **diesel knock** (see rocket combustion later). This point is raised here because diesel engines are beginning to appear in some UAVs and light aircraft, and were already earmarked in Germany for long-range Dornier aircraft during WW2.]

Whereas the normal turbulent flame speed within the cylinder is likely to be about 100 m/s, the equivalent 'flame speed' associated with these muliple spontaneous ignitions of spark knock has been estimated to range from about 200 to 1000 m/s. Within a laboratory flame tube, the **laminar** flame speeds for most hydrocarbons vary little from 0.5 m/s at atmospheric pressure, whereas the velocity of **detonation** comprising mutually supportive flame-and-shock waves may reach 3000 m/s, with accompanying pressure levels of 40 atm).

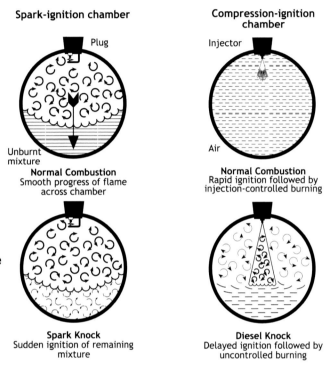

Figure 2
Flame characteristics in piston-engine combustors

Having identified the knock problem in the early years, the urgent requirement was a suitable system of anti-knock rating. Research in UK by Hopkinson, Ricardo, Green, Gibson et al led to a system of rating gasoline in terms of the leannest mixture usable before the onset of knock (this tended to raise the cylinder temperature due to the unconverted heat from the slower combustion, and so promote knock), and this was followed by aiming for a low level of fuel density (favouring those fuels with high spontaneous-ignition temperatures, and thus knock resistance - see Fig. 1). Ricardo devised the variable-compression single-cylinder test engine, and his early approach to fuel rating was to determine the highest useful compression ratio (HUCR) achievable before the onset of knock. However, by expressing the anti-knock characteristic of a fuel sample in terms of a function of the engine rather than the fuel itself led to variation in the rating following changes in ambient conditions. Ricardo therefore proposed the concept of a system of bracketing the sample between blends of two reference fuels so that any such changes should affect all three fuels in a similar manner and maintain their relationship constant.

Initially Ricardo chose toluene and a low anti-knock gasoline to provide the upper and lower limits respectively of his rating scale. Unfortunately, toluene was found to be prone to pre-ignition, whereas successive batches of the reference gasoline could not be guaranteed to match each other.   Parallel research in US by Kettering, Midgley, Edgar, Heron et al culminated in the Waukesha-built CFR (Co-operative Fuel Research) engine incorporating a compression ratio variable from 4:1 to 18:1 during operation (Fig. 3), together with the upper reference fuel of the 2,2,4-trimethylpentane isomer of octane, i-C8H18, plus normal heptane, n-C7H16 as the lower.   The octane number of the test sample is expressed as the volume percentage of iso-octane in the matching reference blend, the blends differing by no more than 2 octane numbers when bracketing the sample These reference fuels are both paraffinic hydrocarbons with similar boiling points (99.3 and 98.4°C) and densities (0.69 and 0.68 kg/L) so that neither property varies significantly over the range of blends.

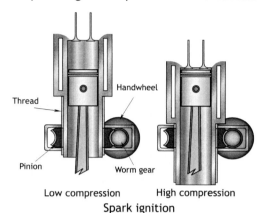

Figure 3
The variable-compression CFR test unit.
Piston at top dead centre.

The geometries of these reference fuel molecules indicate their suitability for the task since this isomer of octane (of which there are 17 variants) is particularly compact, and so able to withstand substantial thermal agitation before disruption.   The molecule of normal heptane, on the other hand, is a long straight chain that cracks relatively easily under stress, revealing unused bonds available for linking with oxygen atoms as a first step in the chain reaction leading towards spontaneous ignition, i.e. spark knock.

iso-octane, iC_8H_{18} (2,2,4-trimethylpentane)
SIT = 415°C
Octane number = 100
UPPER REFERENCE

i.e. $H_3C(CH_2)_5CH_3$
normal heptane, $n\text{-}C_7H_{16}$
SIT = 215°C
Octane number = 0
LOWER REFERENCE

[The reverse situation holds with reference fuels for diesel rating since spontaneous ignition is now a prime requirement.   Hence the upper reference fuel is the straight-chain paraffin normal cetane, $n\text{-}C_{16}H_{34}$, which can be written as $H_3C(CH_2)_{14}CH_3$, whereas the lower reference fuel is an iso-cetane of the form 2,2,4,4 6,8,8-heptamethyl-nonane.]

The intensity of spark knock of a gasoline fuel was measured by means of a bouncing-pin knockmeter, sensitive to the pressure waves of the knocking process, forming part of a circuit with a water voltameter.   This instrumentation circuit was eventually replaced by a pressure-sensitive magnetostriction detector connected to a milliammeter.   The **Research** method of test was introduced in 1930, and the more severe **Motor** method, with its higher mixture temperature of 149°C, in 1932.   The MON of a given sample is thus some 10 numbers below the RON, this temperature-senstive difference being termed the **Research Appreciation**.   The antiknock performance of a gasoline at low speeds and loads is thus represented by the RON, and under severe driving conditions by the MON.

Demands for higher performance in the aviation world stimulated the introduction in 1940 of the **Aviation Lean Mixture** method of anti-knock testing, incorporating a higher coolant temperature and greater ignition advance to simulate cruising conditions. Since combustion temperature is of greater significance at lean mixture, as shown above, a thermal plug was used for detecting knock intensity. (This Lean Mixture method was replaced in 1970 by the Motor method coupled with a set of conversion factors).   The increasing practice of supercharging prompted the introduction in 1941 of the **Aviation Rich Mixture** method, representing maximum power conditions at take-off, climb and combat, utilising a supercharged CFR engine with a fixed compression ratio of 7:1, at conditions adjusted for a slightly audible knock.   Grade rating then consists of both the lean and rich numbers, e.g. Aviation Gasoline Grade 80/87, whereas the Joint Services Designation comprises the lower figure only, e.g. Avgas 80.

Figure 4

The Leaded Gasoline Saga

| 1859 | In US, Drake's well   - start of oil industry |

MOTOR GASOLINE

1903 | **In US, Wright Brothers Flyer - start of first century of powered flight**

1905 | In UK, Ricardo et al - research into **Spark Knock**, and methods of rating fuel.

1916 | In US, Kettering et al - Search for anti-knock **Blending Agents** and **Additives**

Basic fuels were Gasoline and Kerosine - latter suffered from knock.
        Reason: Lower volatility ?
Noted that certain euphorbia plants could withstand winter cold.
        Reason: Red coloration traps additional sunlight ?
Kerosine dyed with Iodine (only dye available at that moment)
        Result: SUCCESS!
Test repeated later with proper red dye.
        Result: FAILURE!!

1920 | Blending with **ANILINE**, but exhaust odour

1921 | **SELENIUM** = 5 x Aniline   } Bad odour imparted to skin and clothes,
TELLURIUM = 20 x Aniline   } leading to threats of staff strike action!
Systematic investigation into at least one compound from all Elements in Periodic Table, using wooden block drilled with holes representing each element, fitted with pegs of lengths indicating anti-knock effectiveness compared with Aniline blending agent.
Result: Emergence of **LEAD** (= 50 x Aniline) as optimal element.
But, toxic, and cylinders fouled.
In US, Midgley - Ethylene **dibromide** scavenger.
But, shortage of BROMINE - hence extracted from sea water.

2000 | In UK, LEAD banned from Mogas (max. 0.005 g Pb/L, cf previous 0.15)

AVIATION GASOLINE

1926	In US,	TEL freely available for Army and Navy.
1930	In US,	Howard issued 87 ON specification
1933	In UK,	87 ON specified with **0.14 g Pb/L**
1936	In US,	100 ON specified
1941	In UK,	100/125 grade specified, supplied from US.
1942	In US,	100/130 grade specified with **0.85 g Pb/L**
1944	In UK,	100/150 grade specified with **1.68 g Pb/L** +Methyl aniline. (Peak!)
1945	In UK,	115/145 grade specified with **1.28 g Pb/L** +Alkylates.
1970	(In UK,	100/130 grade specified with **0.85 g Pb/L**,(Avgas 100)
+	(	100/130 LL grade with **0.56 g Pb/L**, and (Avgas 100LL)
2003	(	80/87 grade with **0.14 g Pb/L** (Avgas 80)

Major contributions to the production of high-octane aviation gasoline include hydrogenation, fluid catalytic cracking, polymerisation and also alkylation, in which an olefin is combined with a paraffin, e.g. isobutene plus isobutane to give isooctane. Coupled with increased concentrations of lead additive, the anti-knock quality of the resulting fuels eventually exceeded that of the isooctane upper reference fuel itself. A partial solution to this problem was found by adding lead to isooctane and rating samples in terms of the lead concentration of the matching leaded reference fuel. But this system proved cumbersome, hence ratings above 100 octane number were then expressed in terms of the more logical **Performance Number**, defined by:

$$\text{Performance Number (PN)} = \frac{(\text{maximum imep of sample})}{(\text{maximum imep of isooctane})} \times 100$$

where imep = indicated mean effective pressure, all measurements being made at the mixture strength related to the peak of the lower of the two bracketing reference fuels.

With this background of fuel anti-knock rating techniques, the fuel-lead saga developed as summarised in Fig 4, and plotted in Fig 5. The nature of the TEL additive itself is illustrated in Fig 6, outlining its mechanism of combating knock.

Figure 5
Development of Avgas anti-knock quality, and lead content.

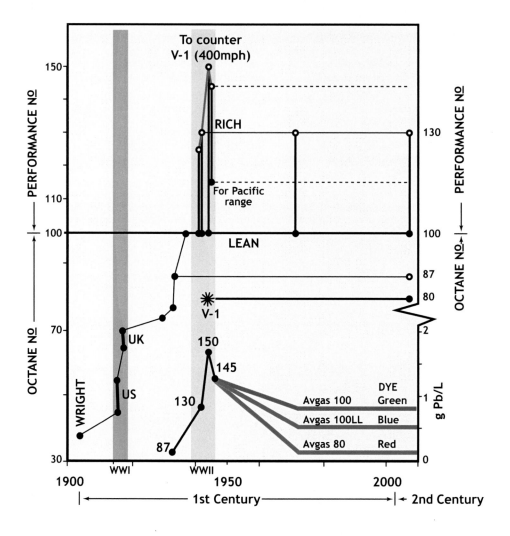

Fig. 6

TETRAETHYL-LEAD

WHAT IS IT?

Metallic **Lead**, **Pb**, cannot dissolve in a liquid hydrocarbon fuel such as Gasoline.

In order to be acceptable, it must be 'coated' with hydrocarbon groups.

Lead is **tetravalent**, hence it can be compounded with **four** hydrocarbon radicals.

The monovalent **ethyl radical**,(C_2H_5-), is commonly used, to give:

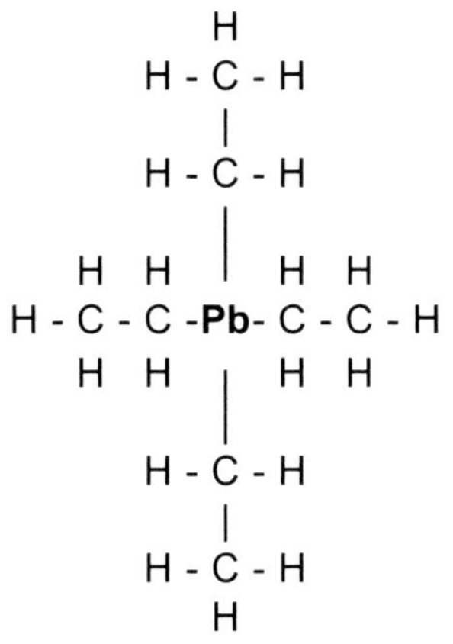

```
                H
            H - C - H
                |
            H - C - H
                |
    H   H       |   H   H
    H - C - C -Pb- C - C - H        tetraethyl-lead,   TEL   (C₂H₅)₄Pb
    H   H   |   H   H
            |
            H - C - H
                |
            H - C - H
                H
```
tetraethyl-lead,   **TEL** $(C_2H_5)_4Pb$

HOW DOES IT WORK?

During the compression stroke, **Lead** is freed from TEL, and oxidises to PbO_2.

On combustion, PbO_2 breaks the incipient knock chain, reducing to **PbO** in the process.

The PbO instantly reoxidises to PbO_2, and continually repeats its chain-breaking process.

Unfortunately, **Lead** remains in the cylinder, causing fouling with refractory salts!

HOW IS LEAD-FOULING AVOIDED?

Bromine, **Br**, provided to scavenge the resulting volatile **Lead-Bromines** with the exhaust.

Again, Bromine must be made acceptable to the liquid hydrocarbon fuel by compounding

with hydrocarbons.   For example:

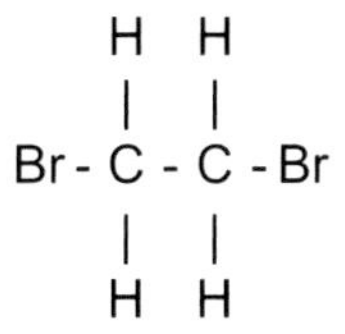

```
        H   H
        |   |
Br - C - C - Br           ethylene dibromide,   EDB,   C₂H₄Br₂
        |   |             (dibromoethane)
        H   H
```
ethylene dibromide,   **EDB**, $C_2H_4Br_2$
(dibromoethane)

Bromine <u>not</u> used in excess, otherwise **corrosion**

7

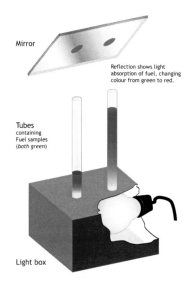

Mirror

Reflection shows light
absorption of fuel, changing
colour from green to red.

Tubes
containing
Fuel samples
(*both green*)

Light box

Figure 7
Demonstration of light absorption by fuel bulk.

Despite the care taken to colour code these three variants of Avgas in order to prevent misfuelling, an interesting incident illustrated that all is not as foolproof as it might appear. A piston-engined aircraft was being refuelled at night and, on completion, the engineer flashed his torch into the tank opening to ensure that he had the correct green Avgas 100 on board and saw, to his horror, that the fuel was red, signifying Avgas 80 which would have meant disaster at take-off. He directed the aircraft to be defuelled, and then noted that the fuel was, in fact, green! Eventually he realised that the light from his torch had passed through the bulk of the fuel, reflected from the bottom of tank, and passed through the fuel again to his eye, much of the spectrum being absorbed except red, the most penetrating colour, as illustrated in Fig. 7.

3.   Enter the Jet Age, Stage Left

For this writer, the introduction to the jet age was dramatic, dangerous and dastardly. Having just arrived home in London for a short leave from the RAF in June 1944, he retired early in eager anticipation of renewing his marital lifestyle.   Imagine his anger when, five minutes later, he was forced to dress and join everyone else in the air-raid shelter on hearing an unfamiliar buzzing noise followed by an eerie silence and then an almighty crash as the first pilotless flying bomb to reach London plunged to Earth somewhere near Bethnal Green, killing three people and wrecking a railway bridge.

Predictably, the writer's thoughts at this juncture were unprintable!   Clearly this meant nothing less than TOTAL WAR, meaning that Hitler would just have to go, making it essential to learn as much as possible about this new weapon - as soon as possible. In this context, Fig. 5 reveals the extremely significant fact that the V-1 was not only a bomb, but also acted as a bombshell in underscoring the arrival of jet propulsion. Although the speed of this aircraft, at 400 mph, was too low to build up sufficient entry air pressure to promote the satisfactory combustion found in a ram jet (hence the requirement for intake valve flaps with a tuned duct),   this speed could not be matched by standard Allied fighters and their fuels, hence the urgent assembly of the following combination:

- the best fighter aircraft available - Typhoon, Tempest, Mosquito, later marks of Spitfire, and Mustang (together with the Meteor jet)

- the best piston engines available - 12 cylinder Rolls-Royce 'V' type Griffon, and 24 cylinder Napier 'H' type sleeve-valve Sabre

- **the best fuel achievable - 100/150 grade aviation gasoline incorporating methyl aniline, water, methanol and additional TEL***

- It is interesting to note that leaded triptane, the 2,2,3-trimethylbutane isomer of heptane, gave an estimated grade rating of no less than 150/270 but proved extremely expensive in terms of crude oil, chlorine reactant and refinery structural steel, and thus not suited to quantity production.   A 115/145 grade was introduced in 1945, largely to improve range for naval aircraft operating in the Pacific.

All this permitted interception, but opening fire was hazardous since the resulting explosion could harm the attacker, hence a technique was devised of wing tipping so that the gyroscope malfunctioned, and the weapon spiralled to Earth

The salient point here is that all the above advanced developments were required in

Figure 8

The V-1 Buzz Bomb

(Derived from http://www.fiddlersgreen.net/AC/aircraft/V1/info/info.php)

Fi-103, FZG 76, Doodle Bug, Farting Fury

Length 25 ft.   Wingspan 17.5 ft.   Warhead 1870 lbm Trialon.   **Speed 400 mph**.
Range 200 miles approx.   Thrust 600 lbf approx.

Propulsion: Pulse jet 500 cycles/min. using **80 Octane Mogas**.

Launched from 152 ft. ramp by steam catapult, or air-dropped from Heinkel He 111.

Over   30,000   manufactured.
        7,500   failed on launch.
      16,500   destroyed by AA guns, balloons and fighters
                 (Typhoons, Tempests, Mosquito, Griffon-Spitfire IX and XIV, Meteor, Mustang)
        6,000   reached targets (London;   from 13 June 1944 to 29 March 1945, also Southampton)

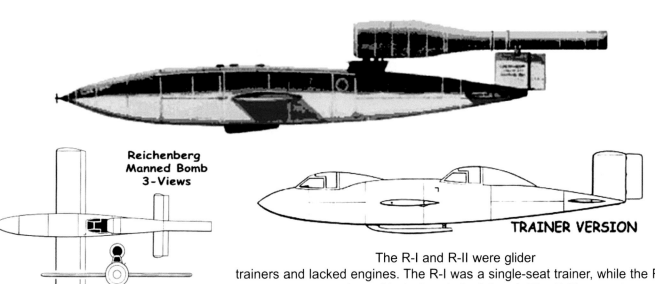

Reichenberg
Manned Bomb
3-Views

TRAINER VERSION

The R-I and R-II were glider
trainers and lacked engines. The R-I was a single-seat trainer, while the R-II
was a two-seat trainer with dual cockpits (above). The R-III was a two-seat
powered trainer, while the R-IV was the operational weapon.

order to counter the menace of the vehicle shown in Fig. 8, comprising:

- a basic and relatively inexpensive winged torpedo

- a simple stove-pipe of a propelling duct, incorporating spring-flap intake valves as the only moving parts

- **a standard 80 octane motor gasoline.**

Clearly, jet propulsion had arrived big time, and this point was reinforced soon afterwards when, serving in France under Operation Overlord, the writer's unit was selected to maintain the Meteor turbojet aircraft operating in that theatre, particular attention being paid to the rear turbine bearings which were reputed to be susceptible to failure.

Following the pioneering work by Whittle in UK, and von Ohain in Germany, various fuels were tested in gas turbine engines and it was found that, with no unique performance parameter comparable to spark knock, satisfactory combustion depended upon a package of property requirements. Gasoline, gas oil, diesel fuel and hydrogen were all explored in initial testing, but kerosine emerged as the front runner. At first, the aero turbine engine was found to be far more fuel-tolerant than its high-performance piston-engine counterpart, but subsequent increases in operating pressures and temperatures rendered the former sensitive also, and so brought the optimal fuel back full circle to the middle distillates, notably kerosine, with quality controlled closely by means of a comparatively large number of specified property limits, eventually totalling about 30 (cf. about 20 for non-aero fuels).

Figure 9

JET FUEL VARIANTS

TYPE	UK (DEF STAN)	NATO	US(MIL)	(CIVIL)	APPLICATION
Kerosine	**Avtur (91-91)**	**F35**	-	**Jet A-1**	**International civil use**
"	-	-	-	Jet A	US only. Freeze -40°C, cf -47
"	Avtur /FSII (91-87)	-	JP-8	-	Military
Wide Cut	Avtag/FSII (91-88)	F34	JP-4	-	Blended with Gasoline (supply)
High Flash	Avcat/FSII (91-86)	F40	JP-5	-	Naval. Fire safety in carriers
		F44			Flash 60°C, cf 38
					[Vietnam, 35% loss, cf. 100% JP-4
Thermal Stability	-	-	-	JPTS	High-flying U2 aircraft
Low Volatility	-	-	-	JP-7	Blackbird aircraft
					Aromatics 3%, cf 25
					ibp 182°C, cf 150
					SE 43.5 MJ/kg , cf 42.8
High Density Synthetic*	-	-	-	JP-10	Gas turbine, or low-drag ramjet missiles
					ED 39.6 MJ/L. cf 34.7
High Density Low Aromatics	-	-	-	RJ-1	Ramjet reference fuel
					0.943 kg/L, cf 0.840 max
					ED 36.7 MJ/L, cf 34.7
Narrow-cut Naphthenic	-	-	-	RP-1	Rocket reference fuel

FSII = Fuel System Icing Inhibitor
SE = Specific Energy (Net)
ED = Energy Density (Net)
ibp = initial boiling point
cf. = comparison with Avtur (JP-8), unless stated otherwise
* Cyclopentadiene

The relatively low volatility of kerosine gives fire safety in handling but necessitates either vaporisation or spraying into the hot combustor flame zone. This fuel is used internationally by airlines under the US civil designation of **Jet A-1**. Despite the vast area of the US, distances within it are still insufficient to permit the fuel to approach freezing, consequently a higher freezing point fuel (**Jet A**) is acceptable for domestic flights. These two fuels are listed in Fig.9

One of the primary requirements of any transport fuel is a high level of available energy. The calorific values on the bases of both gravimetric (**Specific Energy**) and volumetric (**Energy Density**) are plotted in Fig. 10. Since the specific energy of hydrogen is some four times that of carbon, it is no surprise that this property for the hydrocarbon fuels reflects the fall in hydrogen content with increase in density. On the other hand, the energy density rises because, as a mathematical product of specific energy and density, i.e.

$$MJ/kg \times kg/L = MJ/L,$$

the modest fall (10%) in specific energy is outweighed by the relatively large rise (35%) in density. This raises the question of which is the more significant in practice - a factor depending essentially on the application in hand. In subsonic aircraft, for example, mass is dominant, hence a trend towards fuels lighter than kerosine would appear attractive. However, this would increase problems due to volatility in the form of vapour loss, vapour lock and fire safety - so we remain with kerosine. In supersonic aircraft, on the other hand, volume is dominant in order to minimise aerodynamic drag, consequently heavier fuels appear attractive, but this would raise problems of viscosity in the form of increased pumping power, spray droplet size, and early freezing. So once again kerosine emerges as the optimal compromise fuel.

Because the laboratory-determined value of specific energy in a bomb calorimeter involves a temperature rise of a few degrees only, the combustion-produced water condenses and gives its vaporisation enthalpy back to the instrument, hence the result is a **gross** value which is meaningless in practice since engine exhaust products are emitted hot. The correction to the **net** value (typically 3 MJ/kg lower) via the IP manual is therefore strongly recommended.

The development of the main jet-fuel specifications is illustrated in Fig.11. It is interesting to note that the Single Battle Fuel concept of the US Department of Defense led to the use of avtur by all mechanical branches of the

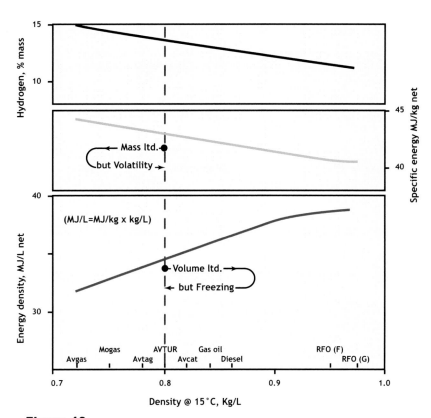

Figure 10
Hydrogen content and calorific values of petroleum fuels.
N.B. Specific energy of nitromethane ($CH_3 NO_2$) = 10.9 MJ/kg, @ density 1.14 kg/L.

services.   With a cetane number ranging from 40 to 49, Avtur lends itself reasonably well to small turbocharged diesel engines ('paraffin pistons'), but problems were reported with smoke generation by battle tanks for concealment in the field.

Figure 11
Development of jet fuel specifications

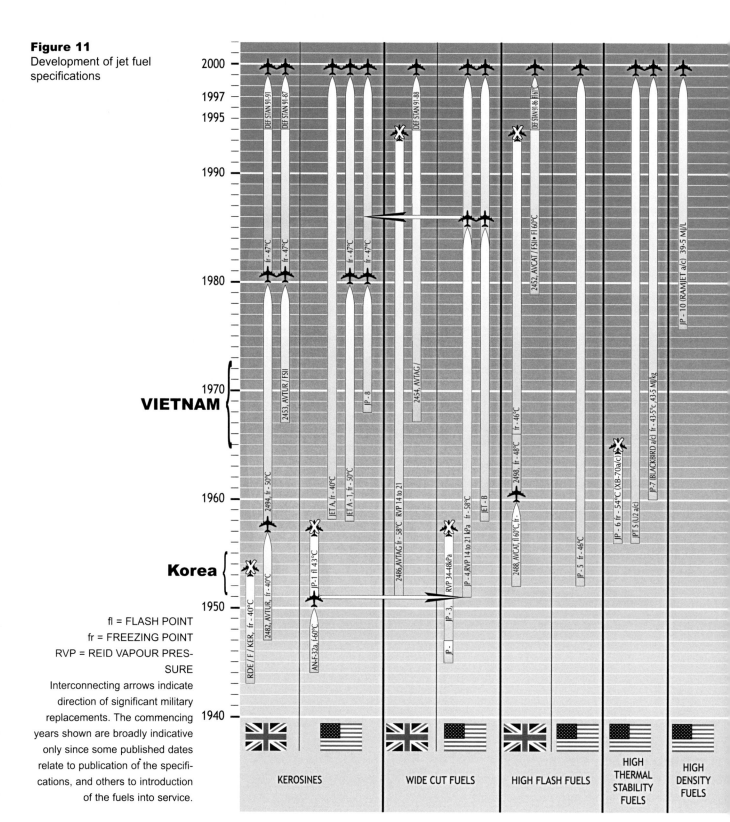

fl = FLASH POINT
fr = FREEZING POINT
RVP = REID VAPOUR PRES-
SURE
Interconnecting arrows indicate direction of significant military replacements. The commencing years shown are broadly indicative only since some published dates relate to publication of the specifications, and others to introduction of the fuels into service.

4. Jet Fuel Additives

Although the kerosines used for service and civilian purposes are fundamentally similar, one difference arises through the handling of possible filter blockage by ice due to the unavoidable traces of water in the fuel. Civil airliners can tolerate the weight and bulk of fuel-filter heaters, but the services prefer the addition of a fuel-system icing inhibitor, **FSII**, (diethylene glycol monomethyl ether, $CH_3OCH_2CH_2OCH_2CH_2OH$) to the fuel itself. Furthermore, in an attempt to maintain the cleanness of aircraft and engine fuel systems, and thus avoid blockage of injectors by rust particles, a polar corrosion inhibitor is added. This practice was once discontinued after the discovery of the inherent water hold-up tendency. However, the rash of stiction problems that followed led to the realisation that this additive also acted as a lubricity enhancer, consequently it was reinstated under the title of Corrosion Inhibitor/Lubricity Improving Additive, **CI/LIA**, but now simply as **LIA**. Avtur incorporating these two additives was given the US military designation of **JP-8**. One further drawback of the presence of water in kerosine is the blockage of filters by an aerobic fungal layer generated at the interface of the fuel and the underlying water. These microorganisms are known colloquially as 'Hydrocarbon Utilising Microbes' or 'HUM-bugs', whereas airline captains tend to describe them as 'mushroom soup'. **Biostat** additives inhibit the growth of fungus and bacteria, whereas **biocides** kill them. Fortuitously, FSSI in military fuels also acts as a biostat, whereas civil aircraft systems are treated with a boron compound over a three-day incubation period during maintenance inspections.

The emergence of jet propulsion for aircraft was recognised worldwide, and the clamour for copious suppplies of Aviation Turbine Fuel (Avtur) began. Having been geared up for the bulk production of high quality Avgas, there was no possibility of this demand being met adequately in the short term. As a stop gap, therefore, it was decided to augment the supply of jet fuel by blending the components of both Avgas and Avtur into a single product entitled Wide Cut Fuel (**Avtag**), known as **JP-4** when additised with FSII and LIA. Despite its intended short term life before the demand for Avtur could be met, Avtag still survives today, but is relegated to the military and to cold climates rather than the airlines. The Navy, on the other hand, has a particular need for a jet fuel with a flammability, and thus volatility, lower than normal in order to avoid the possibility of dangerous concentrations of vapour build-up within the cavities of the aircraft carrier. This High-Flash kerosine was designated as **Avcat** and, when additised with FSII and LIA, as **JP-5**.

The complement of additives permitted/mandatory in jet fuels also includes the following:

Antioxidants - Unstable components (e.g. olefins/alkenes) can oxidise during storage to form gums, any naturally-occurring antioxidants in the fuel having been unavoidably removed during hydroprocessing.

Metal Deactivating Additives (MDA) - Ions of heavy metals catalyse oxidation, causing corrosion, gum formation, and loss of thermal stability.

Static Dissipator Additives (SDA) - Trace polar contaminants, water and dirt lead to charge separation and streaming electrical current during refuelling, generating high gradients of electrostatic potential in the fuel tank, particularly at low temperatures, with the potential of sparks promoting explosions if the air-vapour mixture in the ullage space is within the flammable range.

Leak Detecting Additives - Assist in locating leaks in ground-based fuel handling systems.

5. Higher Performance Jet Fuels

These first five turbine fuels shown if Fig. 9 can be considered as the primary members of the conventional civil and service jet fuel menus, but advanced versions then emerged for specific purposes related to more severe operating conditions. At higher Mach numbers, for example, kinetic heating from the air being brought to rest relative to the aircraft means that the fuel is subjected to abnormally high temperatures for significant periods. Furthermore, in the absence of cooling air, a heat sink for the lubricating oil and various electronic items could be provided only by commandeering the fuel, which further compromises its stability. Since multi-bonding in the hydrocarbon molecules, as with olefins for example, represents instability, fuel components had to be selected carefully to produce fuels of high thermal stability. The resultant fuel was described as 'Jet Propulsion, Thermal Stability' (**JPTS**), and used for the U2 aircraft operating at high altitude A thermally-stable fuel of low volatility was also needed for the very high altitude Blackbird Mach 3+ aircraft, requiring a higher specific energy in addition. This was designated as **JP-7**, with reduced quantities of aromatics and impurities such as sulphur, nitrogen and oxygen, together with higher hydrogen content, density and flash point.

With the widening applications to high-speed missiles, interest turned to individual hydrocarbons to provide the desired properties. The resulting cyclopentadiene was designated as **JP-10**, with an improved energy density relative to Avtur, intended for either gas turbine or ramjet propulsion. Further attempts to increase the energy density of the fuel include:

- Other individual hydrocarbons such as cyclododecane, decalin, 9-methylperhyfluorene, adamantine, Shelldyne H, and H-COT D.

- Hydrides with carbon replaced by more energetic elements, such as boron, beryllium, lithium, magnesium, aluminium and titanium.

- Slurries of solid particles of the above elements in a high-energy carrier fluid.

A more widely-available ramjet reference fuel was developed under the designation RJ-1, differing from Avtur with a higher density, narrower distillation range at higher level, higher freezing point, and much reduced contents of aromatics and olefins.

For rocket engine performance analysis, a narrow cut of kerosine with most properties lying between those for Avtur and **RJ-1** has been developed with the designation **RP-1**.

6. Specific Impulse

In piston-engine operation, the full combustion temperature of about 2300 K applies for only part of the thermodynamic cycle, hence no additional air need be entrained for cooling the combustion gases. In gas-turbine operation, however, this temperature applies continuously, hence some 70% of the entry air is reserved to protect the combustor wall and cool the combustion gases down to the maximum of about 1350 K that the nozzle guide vanes and turbine blades can accommodate (higher if internally cooled). With ramjets, on the other hand, no such constraints arise in the absence of downstream hardware. As a result, the dissociation that occurs at temperatures above about 1700 K becomes increasingly significant, and this, together with any subsequent recombination occurring in the propelling duct, can dominate the resulting thrust. This feature is even more relevant in rocketry where combustion takes place with diluent-free oxidants, and temperatures correspondingly range from about 2850 to 4700 K.

The performance of reactants selected for such engines is therefore rated more accurately than on specific energy alone by expressing the stream thrust exerted at the nozzle throat on a basis of unit mass flow rate of the propelling products, and this is known as the **Specific Impulse**, I_s, with units of N s/kg, as illustrated in Fig. 12.

[Note, 1 lbf s/lbm = 1 'second' = 9.807 N s/kg]

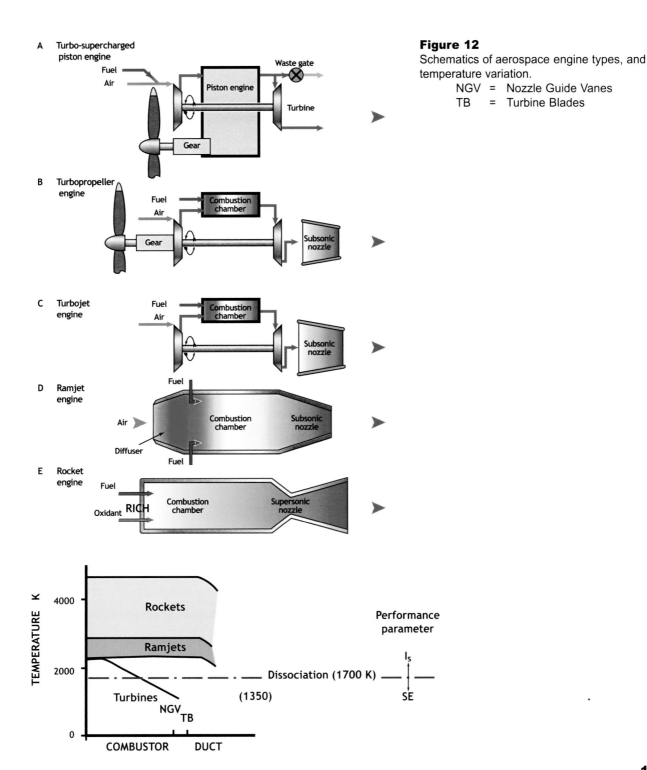

Figure 12
Schematics of aerospace engine types, and temperature variation.
NGV = Nozzle Guide Vanes
TB = Turbine Blades

Applying the Bernouilli expression to the gas flow through the nozzle leads to a mathematical derivation of specific impulse in terms of $\sqrt{(Tc/Mp)}$ and functions of the index gamma, where:

Tc = combustion temperature,

Mp = mean molar mass of propelling gases, and

gamma = ratio of specific heats, cp/cv

consequently reactants giving the highest combustion temperature and the lowest molar masses and gamma are sought. I_s may be calculated based on either:

- 'shifting' equilibrium allowing for changes in product composition throughout expansion in the nozzle, or

- 'frozen' equilibrium assuming no further chemical changes downstream of the combustor.

The former exceeds the latter typically by about 5%.

For ramjets, specific impulse may be expressed on either:

- the air mass flow rate, which establishes engine size for a given level of thrust, or

- the fuel mass flow rate, which indicates aircraft range for a given fuel mass,

whereas for rockets, the thrust per unit mass flow rate of fuel-plus-oxidant is employed.

Values are also available on a reactant volumetric basis (comparable to Energy Density) and given the term **Density Impulse, I_d**, with units of N s/L.

[Note: 1 gf s/cc = 1 kgf s/L = 9.807 N s/L]

7. Chemical Rocket Reactants

For flight at higher speeds, and for operation in space, rocket propulsion is necessary, independent of atmospheric oxygen. Hence, in a chemically-energised rocket vehicle, the reactants have to perform both energy release and propulsive thrust, which are likely to present conflicting demands for simultaneous high Tc plus low Mp and gamma. (This constraint involved with a single pair of reactant materials is eased when the reactants and propellant are entirely independent, as discussed later). Low molar-mass hydrogen is therefore an attractive propellant as well as a fuel and, in fact, recent work on chemical 'tri-propellant' rockets is based on the addition of hydrogen to a reactant pair in order to reduce the molar mass of the propellant product as well as supplying additional reaction energy. This not only improves combustion efficiency, but also increases specific impulse significantly while reducing soot, noise and vehicle weight. However, some problems of explosion and toxicity have been reported.

The major chemical fuels and oxidants of interest in rocketry are tabulated in Fig. 13, in descending order of the peak values of specific impulse determined when plotted against mixture density. (The relative values indicate a significant difference between specific impulse and specific energy, underlining the importance of the former for accurate assessments). These peak values of I_s and I_d are plotted against their related

Figure 13

REPRESENTATIVE CHEMICAL ROCKET REACTANTS

Derived from Rocketdyne,California

Note: Chamber pressure of 1000 psia, expanding to 14.7 psia with shifting equilibrium

FUELS

Name	Formula	SE	With **Oxygen**			
		MJ/kg	Peak I_s kN s/kg	d kg/L	Peak I_d kN s/L	d kg/L
Liquid Hydrogen	LH_2	120.0	3.83	0.28	1.69	0.65
Hydrazine *	N_2H_4	16.7	3.07	1.07	3.29	1.07
UDMH	$(CH_3)_2N_2H_2$	30.1	3.04	0.98	2.98	0.99
RP-1	$C_{12.5}H_{24.6}$	43.5	2.94	1.02	3.02	1.03
Ammonia	NH_3	18.6	2.88	0.89	2.56	0.89
Ethanol (92.5%)	C_2H_5OH	26.8	2.82	0.99	2.80	1.00

Hypergolic with HTP, and RFNA (spontaneously ignitable on contact, but delay critical!)

UDMH = Unsymmetrical Dimethyl Hydrazine

OXIDANTS

Name	Formula	With **RP-1**			
		Peak I_s kN s/kg	d kg/L	Peak I_d kN s/L	d kg/L
Liquid Oxygen	LO_2	2.94	1.02	3.02	1.03
Nitrogen Tetroxide	N_2O_4	2.71	1.25	3.41	1.27
Hydrogen Peroxide, HTP	H_2O_2	2.68	1.30	3.48	1.31
Nitric Acid, RFNA	HNO_3	2.63	1.35	3.56	1.36
Chlorine Trifluoride	ClF_3	2.53	1.41	3.79	1.68

HTP = High Test Peroxide

RFNA = Red Fuming Nitric Acid

Figure 13

FUELS + OXIDANTS

'Oxidation' = loss of one or more electrons, increasing positive valency

Fuel	Peak I_s kN s/kg		
	With **Oxygen**	With **Fluorine**	d kg/L
Hydrogen	**3.83**	**4.02**	0.45
Hydrazine	**3.07**	**3.56**	1.31
Ammonia	**2.88**	**3.50**	1.18

MONOPROPELLANTS

Derived from
G P Sutton, Rocket propulsion elements, John Wiley & Sons 1963
S F Sarner, Propellant chemistry, Reinhold Publishing Company, 1966
I Glassman & R F Sawyer, The performance of chemical propellants, AGARDOgraph 129, January 1970

Reactant	Formula	Density @ 20°C, kg/L	I_s kN s/kg	I_d kN s/L	Reaction Temperature K
Nitromethane	CH_3NO_2	1.12	**2.49**	3.13	2467
UDMH	$(CH_3)_2N_2H_2$	0.78	**1.96**	1.53	1154
Hydrazine	N_2H_4	1.01	**1.94**	1.96	905
Tetranitromethane	$C(NO_2)_4$	1.64	**1.78**	2.91	2170
HTP	H_2O_2	1.44	**1.62**	2.33	1278

Figure 13

SOLID REACTANTS

Derived from

J Humphries, Rockets and guided missiles, Ernest Benn Ltd., 1956

J E Daboo. Solid-fuel rocket propulsion, Temple Press, 1962

G P Sutton, Rocket propulsion elements, John Wiley & Sons, 1963

Type	Typical examples	General properties	I_s kN s/kg	I_d kN s/L	Burning rate cm/s
Single base colloidal	Nitrocellulose	Cool burning, hygroscopic. Detonable.			
Double base colloidal	Nitrocellulose plasticised with nitroglycerine Extruded or cast	Nitric esters detonable, but stabilise each other Not case bondable	1.57 - 2.25	2.51 - 5.65	0.3 - 2.2
Composite	Pressed - black powder Plastic - ammonium perchlorate with polyisobutene binder Polymerisable binder - rubbers	Not case bondable Case bondable Case bondable	1.67 - 2.16 1.67 - 2.35	2.81 - 3.63 2.81 - 3.95	0.3 - 1.3 0.3 - 3.8
Composite modified double base	Inorganic oxidant with nitrocellulose binder	High performance Case bondable	2.35 - 2.54	4.14 - 4.47	0.8 - 2.5

Notes:

1. Densities vary from about 1.6 to 1.8 kg/L

2. Combustion temperatures range from about 1400 to 4000 K

3. Addition of aluminium, beryllium or lithium improves performance

4. Commercial dynamite = nitroglycerine absorbed in sawdust

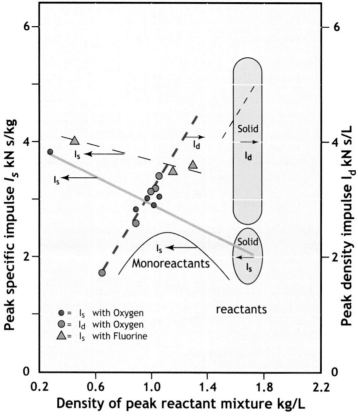

Figure 14
Variation of peak specific impulse and peak density impulse with
related mixture densities.
(Derived from Rocketdyne, California.
J.E. Dabro, Solid fuel rocket propulsion, Temple Press, 1962.
G.P. Sulton, Propellant chemistry, Reinhold Publishing Co., 1966)

mixture densities in Fig. 14 which, nevertheless, show some similarity with the variations in calorific values in Fig. 10, prompting similar broad conclusions.   It follows that the first stage of a multi-stage rocket requiring a high Id to minimise drag would benefit from a heavy mixture such as hydrazine or RP-1 paired with HTP or chlorine trifluoride.   For later stages in space, however, the favoured reactant pair for high Is would be the lighter members such as liquid hydrogen and liquid oxygen.   Also shown are the marked improvements when replacing liquid oxygen with liquid fluorine.   Certain fuel-oxidant pairs are 'hypergolic' (ignite spontaneously on contact), but a minimal delay is essential in order to avoid a disastrous 'hard start' comparable in principle to diesel knock. Hypergolic ignition delay can be measured accurately by

means of the twin-jet rig (Fig. 15a) in which horizontal jets of the two reactants are arranged to impinge whilst falling under gravity.   The distances fallen from the jet level to 1) the point of impingement, and 2) the point of ignition, are converted to time durations by means of Newton's law of motion:

$$s = ut + 0.5gt^2$$

where
  $s = $ distance fallen

  $t = $ time duration of fall

  $u = $ initial vertical velocity $= 0$ in this case

  $g = $ acceleration due to gravity $= 980.7$ cm/s2

Hence,   Ignition delay $= t_2 - t_1 = 45.16 (\sqrt{s_2} - \sqrt{s_1})$ ms

A typical value is 60 ms. for hydrazine hydrate and hydrogen peroxide.

The simplicity and inherent reliability of a liquid rocket engine can be improved, together with a reduction in mass, by the adoption of a monopropellant to provide energy by means of either a decomposition or self-oxidation, but this is at the expense of performance. The volume of a monoreactant is reduced to a minimum by storage in the solid phase within the combustor itself. The charge 'grain' is commonly shaped into one of a number of geometrical cross-sectional patterns which, together with inhibition of some selected surfaces, ensure that the surface area exposed to combustion does not vary appreciably in order to promote constant thrust throughout the burn.

The rate of burning of a solid reactant can be determined by means of the strand burner (Fig 15b) which incorporates a reactant strand of 3.175 mm diameter, drilled transversely to accommodate an ignition wire and two timing wires displaced typically at 12.7 cm. The strand is mounted vertically in a sealed vessel which is then charged with nitrogen at the required pressure. After actuation of the ignition wire, the strand burns downwards in cigarette fashion, side-burning being prevented by prior double-dipping in a plastic fluid. The interval between the severing of the two timing wires permits calculation of the combustion rate.

Figure 15
Schematic of combustion performance testing of rocket reactants

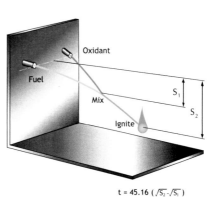

$$t = 45.16 \left(\sqrt{S_2} - \sqrt{S_1} \right)$$

a) Twin jet rig for hypergolic liquid reactants

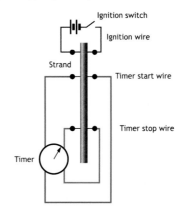

b) Strand burner for solid reactants

8. 2003 - WELCOME TO THE SECOND CENTURY OF AEROSPACE

In the writer's view, the transition from the first to the second aerospace century was no marked by any positive Earth-shattering event comparable to the success of the Wrigh brothers in 1903.   Nevertheless, some activities that had been simmering away during the closing years of the first century came to the boil with practical effects at the start of the second.   There was also the melancholy demise of that classic aircraft, Concorde, which had proved to be a marvel of both technology and Anglo-French co-operation. However, since it was not paying its way, it had to follow leaded fuels and leave the stage - in September 2003 - but for reasons of economics rather than health. (Interestingly, a group of retired pilots plans to resurrect a Concorde, and operate it as a heritage aircraft - *Bonne chance*, and *Good luck*)!   Also, the ocean claimed the solar-powered Helios multi-propellered flying wing following self-induced oscillations caused b' failure of the electronic and flight-control systems

Some of the many ongoing activities showing promise with the arrival of the new century include chemical relight at high altitude, enhanced oxidation control, alternative fuels, fuel testing techniques and advanced propulsion, as outlined below.

9. Chemical Relight at Altitude

The traditional method of high-altitude turbine relight is not considered efficient because the fuel-air radicals generated by applying a large electrical current tend to recombine rapidly.   Leeds University is therefore exploring the potential of effecting ignition chemically by adapting the technique of spontaneous oxidation, comparable to hypergolic ignition in rocket reactants, used by the 2.5 cm long Bombardier beetle.   This remarkable insect pumps a mixture of aqueous solutions of hydroquinone, $C_6H_6O_2$, and hydrogen peroxide, H_2O_2, into a 1 mm reaction chamber where the mixture is catalysed by crystals of peroxidase and catalase derived from enzyme glands within the chamber walls, and then discharged at 500 cycles/second as a 30 cm jet of steam and benzoquinone, $C_6H_4O_2$, at 100°C from twin nozzles at the versatile tip of its abdomen with pinpoint accuracy against predators [1].

10. Oxidation Control for Thermal Stability and Fire Safety

Any increase in the maximum operating fuel temperature permitted at the burner inlet will extend the heat capacity of the fuel; an increase of 56K (100°F), for example, resulting in an improvement of 50%.   Consequently, the High Temperature Thermal Stability (HiTTS) project features a 'JP-8 +100' fuel incorporating an additive package of anti-oxidants, metal deactivators, detergents and dispersants.

The probable cause of the TWA Flight 800 crash in 1996 was eventually traced to a short-circuit outside the near-empty centre fuel tank that allowed voltages to enter through the contents wiring.   The shock waves that followed throughout the industry led to warnings from Boeing regarding possible faulty fuel pumps, and an order from the FAA concerning inspections and recommendations to keep the pumps covered at all times.   Later, the FAA issued a notice of proposed rulemaking to reduce the chance of catastrophic fuel tank explosions by means of either flammability reduction (by tank inerting with nitrogen to reduce the concentration of oxygen to 12%) or ignition mitigation (by either polyurethane foam filling or explosion suppression)   This proposal met some resistance from cash-strapped airlines but, after pressure from the National Transportation Safety Board, these regulations were due to be finalised in September 2007, consequently more positive steps towards the fire safety of central fuel tanks are expected soon in this second century.

An early project at Cranfield University comprised sampling from the primary zone of a gas-turbine combustor to provide a continuous source of low-oxygen purge gas, using the incoming fuel to cool the sampling probe. In the Boeing 7E7 aircraft, a method has been designed to take air from the environmental control system, reduce its oxygen content, and then distribute it to a venting installation [2]. Also, the PhostrEx bromine system has been demonstrated to extinguish a fire in less than one tenth of a second [3].

11. Alternative Fuels

Activities with alternative fuels in the road-transport sector that had grown during the latter years of the first century were now being given serious consideration to either augment or replace aviation kerosine. This is no simple task since kerosine has been seen to be an optimal blend for aero gas turbine engines. The alternative-fuel scene is therefore being re-examined closely with aviation in mind.

Aviation fuels have traditionally been derived from petroleum sources, but these are not likely to endure for more than about 40 years. Of the various candidate alternatives, the following groups appear to be the most significant:

Supplemental fuels.   Petroleum-type fuels derived from non-petroleum sources.

Substitute fuels.   Non-petroleum type fuels.

11.1 Supplemental Fuels

As far as conventional fossil hydrocarbon sources are concerned, a broad-brush assessment of their potential lifetimes is available from the quotient of the known reserves and the current annual consumption rate. Although inherently imprecise, this Reserves:Production 'life index' parameter is given some credence by the following factors:

- reserves are likely to rise as more sources are discovered, and existing extraction percentages increase through improved technology plus the pressures of higher prices of conventional fuels.

- consumption rates inevitably climb in step with improving standards of living in both developed and developing countries.

Hence, these values would not be expected to change greatly in the medium term. Fig. 16 shows, in fact, that the R:P parameters for the three main fossil fuels remained sensibly constant over the last few decades, until the beginning of this second century has seen an eventual dip for coal, due both to a reduction in resources, and a rise in consumption rate.

Natural gas, coal and/or biomatter can be

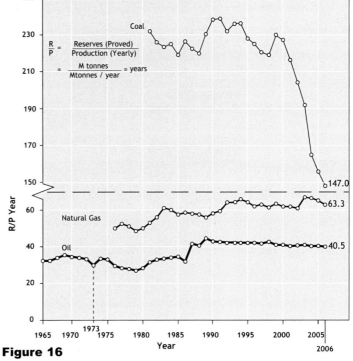

Figure 16
Worldwide Reserves-Production ratios
(Derived from BP Amoco)

23

converted to Avtur by the various routes illustrated in Fig. 17. The **natural gas** route, for example, has been adopted by Boeing for testing in a B-52H aircraft since this has independent fuel systems for each pod comprising two P&W TF33 engines. A 50/50 blend with JP-8 has been selected to compensate for the absence of aromatics in the synthetic fuel in relation to seal swelling. No immediate change in performance was noted apart from less smoke apparent at take-off, but subsequently less coke deposits were found, with reductions of 1% in fuel burn, 1.6% in CO_2, and 90% in particulates. That aircraft has now been flown with all eight engines fuelled with this blend, and cold-weather trials completed successfully at temperatures down to -22°C. Afterburning tests are to follow which, if successful, should herald the emergence of a natural-gas sourced supplemental aviation kerosine early in this century [**4**].

Figure 7

ALTERNATIVE FUELS

Main types: **Supplemental and Substitute**

Type	Characteristics	Examples	
SUPPLEMENTAL	Petroleum-type fuels from non-petroleum sources	Avtur from **NG**	(50% Boeing B-52H, US)
		Avtur from **Coal**	(Sasol, S. Africa)
		Avtur from **Biomatter**	(Babassu, Brazil) (Beacon Energy, China) (Boeing 10%) (N.Dakota University)

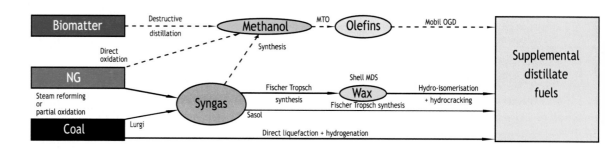

Type	Characteristics	Examples
SUBSTITUTE	Non-petroleum type fuels	**Alcohols** But **Methanol, CH$_3$OH** , 50% Oxygen mass [A380 ~ 250 t fuel, !] **Nitromethane, CH$_3$NO$_2$** But 75% (Oxygen + Nitrogen) mass Hence SE only 10 MJ/kg, cf 43.3 [See engine] **Liquid Hydrogen**, SE 120.2 MJ/kg,(!) But ED only 8.59 MJ/L, cf 34.7 & bp -252.7°C (cryogenics), cf 150-260 [Plus Contrails!]

NG = Natural Gas

SE = Specific Energy (net)

ED = Energy Density (net)

cf. = comparison with Avtur

Another alternative source is **coal**, which still has the advantage of a relatively high life index despite its recent fall.   In South Africa, SASOL uses an indirect method to convert coal to 'syngas' (CO + H$_2$) via the Lurgi process, followed by a Fischer-Tropsch shift reaction with a catalyst to produce waxes, oils, engine fuels and oxygen-containing chemicals. Avtur containing up to 50% Sasol fuel has been approved for current use, and Sasol is now seeking approval for 100% concentration, containing at least 8% of aromatics [5].   Shale oil and tar represent additional sources of hydrocarbons, and large deposits are known to exist worldwide so that, despite their processing difficulties, they could well figure significantly within this second century.

The third supplemental fuel source is the range of carbohydrates in **biomatter**, which has the fundamental advantages, of course, of perpetual availability and carbon neutrality.   Extraction of useful triglycerides from vegetation is undertaken either by pressing or by solvent action, an effective process being to react them with alcohols to form methyl esters.

In Brazil, the babassu palm tree has proved to be a source of biokerosine which was found to possess high levels of lubricity and detergency, as well as ameliorating the loss of turbine power at altitude due to the presence of oxygen in the molecule [6].   In China, the UK firm Beacon Energy is bidding to start production of a synthetic aviation kerosine from biomatter, to be priced at about 70% of conventional fuel [7].   Boeing is including 10% of biofuel in kerosine, and checking freezing at altitude [8].   The University of North Dakota is developing a synthetic JP-8 kerosine from crop oils [9].   Another source of interest is blue-green algae and other products of aquatic energy farming. Algae are plants that live in shallow water, not necessarily fresh, depending on light for existence., They need less area than ground crops, giving 94 000 L/ha, i.e.150 times more than soya beans [10].   In all the above ventures, of course, the overriding target must always be the achievement of an optimal balance in crop use for the production of both food and fuel, without damage to the biosphere.

Prediction No. 1 Aviation kerosine will remain largely petroleum-based for about 40 years, but supplies will continue to be supplemented progressively from natural gas, coal, the large deposits of shale oil and tar, and perpetually-available biomatter. Algae appear particularly promising, and wild grasses perhaps even more so, whereas genetic engineering may permit the design of a perfect crop for a fuel source, with the needs for cultivation space eased by partial terraforming of the desert using seawater, combined with aerial re-vegetation by dropping seedlings in liquid-filled containers.

11.2 Substitute Fuels

Of those fuels differing substantially from the petroleum conventionals, the following two appear to offer possibilities.

11.2.1 Alcohols

The monohydric alcohol molecule consists of some hydrocarbon radical, R, bonded with a single hydroxyl group, OH, giving the general formula ROH, the most common being those based on the alkanes (paraffins), thus described as alkanols. The first two members are methanol (wood alcohol) CH_3OH, and ethanol (grain alcohol) C_2H_5OH. In comparison with conventional aviation fuels, the main advantages are as follows:

- Obtainable from vegetable matter, hence perpetual availability

- Carbon neutrality since combustion-generated CO_2 absorbed by subsequent crops (but emissions from harvesting must be included).

- Lower carbon content

- Lower freezing point

- High flash point of ethanol improving fire safety in handling

- Low flame luminosity increasing engine life

- High octane rating for S-I piston engine use

On the other hand, the main drawbacks are as follows:

- Lower specific energy and energy density reducing range for given tankage size

- Polar, hence tendency to attack materials of fuel system

- Poor lubricity, and lubricants attacked

- Combustion-generated aldehyde emissions

Alcohols are routinely produced by oxidation, reforming or hydrolysis of fossil feedstock, but ethanol can be derived economically from a varity of vegetable sources such as wheat, sugar beet and sawdust. Pilot plants now consist of plastic pipes containing microalgae that photosynthesise with CO_2 to form sugars, and convert them to ethanol and biodiesel [**11**]. (One notes with some melancholy that, due to the worldwide glut of wine, the price fall in France has led to many millions of litres, including some of the higher grades, being turned into vinegar and ethanol, the latter being blended with gasoline - *Sacrebleu!*) [**12**]

The high RON values (114 and 111) of these first two alcohols make them attractive for spark-ignition piston engines: in Brazil, the 225 kW Lycoming-powered Ipanema crop duster became the first aircraft to be certified to fly on ethanol, with 1000 of these aircraft delivered in 2005, winning a Flight International Award in that year. The plan is to convert all 90 such aircraft in the Brazilian Air Force [13].

In air-breathing continuous combustion, the oxygen content of these fuels offers some advantages in reducing unburnt emissions, and alcohols have been found to burn satisfactorily in gas-turbine engines. However, from the handling viewpoint, the oxygen content is an embarrassment, as is indicated dramatically in the case of a large jet aircraft. The Airbus A380, for example, carries just under 250 tonnes of fuel (giving a fuel:max. take-off weight ratio of 0.44) and, should this be methanol, some 125 tonnes of oxygen would be involved which, of course, are available free from the surrounding atmosphere.

In rocketry, on the other hand, the need to carry oxygen is vital, but it is less important if some is included within the fuel tank rather than the oxidant tank, hence the situation turns full circle, and alcohols have a place here. In fact, ethanol was used in both the German V-2 (Fig. 18) and the US Viking vehicles.

Figure 18

The V-2 Rocket Vehicle

(Derived from http://www.zamandayolculuk.com/cetinbal/V2RROCKET.htm)

Vergeltungswaffe (Reprisal Weapon) 2

Length 46 ft. Diameter 65 inch. Warhead 1650 lbm. Loaded Weight 20 500 lbm.

Thrust 56 000 lbf. Flight Duration 1 minute. Range 200 miles. Altitude 70 miles.

Dive speed 3000 mph !!

Fuel: Ethanol. Oxidant: Liquid Oxygen

Hydrogen peroxide (reacted with calcium permanganate) to generate steam for 500 hp turbine to drive reactant pumps.

Over 5000 built, production being undertaken round the clock in former calcium sulphate mines at gunpoint by some 60 000 slaves, over 20 000 of whom died from the harsh conditions, or were hanged on von Braun's orders when sabotage was suspected.

September 1944: launched against liberated Paris, then London and Antwerp

Militarily ineffective. Guidance system primitive, and costs equivalent to a four-engined bomber which was accurate, with longer range, carried more warheads and was reusable.

The author enjoying a 'virtual' flight on Cranfield's own V-2

Photograph by permission of Brian N. Hunt FBIIP., FRPS

(It is noteworthy that those of us on the receiving end of the V-2 witnessed an intriguing - if nonreassuring - phenomenon. Because of the colossal speed of approach, the 'whoosh' of the descent was heard **after** the explosion at the target rather than the other way round, in a rather quirky reversal of time. It is remarkable how one can register such an event when one is scared stiff!)

> **Prediction No. 2** Vegetable-based alcohols, possibly produced via solar energy, will endure for light piston-engined aircraft, including UAVs, and for some less intensive rockets, but will not apply to main gas turbine engines.

11.2.2 Hydrogen

Diatomic hydrogen, H_2, represents the simplest structure of a fuel molecule, and is attractive for its abundance (ninth in terms of mass, and third in terms of numbers of atoms) throughout the biosphere. Although industrial quantities of hydrogen gas are currently derived most economically from fossil sources, commercial quantities may eventually be realised by the electrolysis of water, with catalytic assistance, energised by waste heat from nuclear plants, by sunlight, or from indigenous hydroelectric sources as in Iceland [**14**]. Liquefaction can be achieved by cooling with liquid nitrogen below the inversion level of 205 K, followed by expanding through a throttling valve.

In comparison with conventional aviation fuels, the main advantages of hydrogen are as follows:

- Outstandingly high level of net specific energy

- High flame speed (particularly useful for scramjets).

- Wide range of flammability, aiding transient operation

- Emissions restricted to H_2O and some NOx, with no carbon products.

- Few problems of fuel spray or vaporisation in the combustor.

- Low emissivity of flame, minimising metal temperatures and thermal stress, increasing engine life.

- Non toxic and non carcinogenic.

- Any leaks disperse rapidly.

- Effectiveness as a heat sink for cooling hot components due to superior heat transfer properties and high specific heat capacity as liquid, the absorbed heat being available regeneratively for prevaporisation (particularly useful for supersonic flight).

- Electrochemical activity higher than that for hydrazine, oxygenates or hydrocarbons (valuable for fuel cells).

- High spontaneous ignition temperature (574°C cf 470 Avgas), and thus potential knock resistance.

On the other hand, the main drawbacks are as follows:

- Very low density, entailing high storage volumes, unless gas compressed (typically to 700 bar) or combined chemically with a metal alloy. Alternatively some 18% of volume may be saved if the liquid fuel is stored as a slush with suspended frozen particles.

- High volatility due to extremely low boiling point, hence potential for boil-off in storage and, with wide range of flammability, fire danger in handling.

- Very low boiling point promotes risk of cryogenic burns to flesh.

- Very low net energy density.

- Lower luminosity flame despite high temperature - impedes fire safety.

- Leakages could reach the tropopause and destroy the methane-scrubbing OH radicals, and also the stratosphere leading to the halogen destruction of ozone.

- The small molecules of hydrogen can penetrate small gaps in so-called 'flameproof' equipment..

- Piston engine power reduced because intake air displaced by gaseous fuel.

- Despite high level of spontaneous ignition temperature, fairly strong tendencies to pre-ignition, backfiring and spark knock due to low ignition energy (0.019 mJ, cf 0.4 Avgas) and higher combustion temperature (2431 K, cf 2298 Avgas).

The curves in Fig.19 show that, with the few exceptions of hydrogen and nitromethane, the specific energies of the (stoichiometric) fuel-air mixtures vary little from 2.9 MJ/kg, and that the combustion temperatures also lie within a relatively narrow range of 2250 to 2430 K. In these contexts, therefore, engines are comparatively independent of fuel type, whereas aircraft fuel systems are not.

The early history of piston-engine use of hydrogen appears to stem from Ricardo's attempt to feed airship diesel engines with the gas vented to maintain buoyancy by compensating for the consumed gas oil. In the automotive world at the end of the first fuel century, BMW conducted tests on 12-cylinder piston engines with the injection valves integrated into the inlet manifolds, and the cylinders air cooled to avoid preignition [15], whereas Mazda unveiled its Renesis dual-fuel rotary engine, powered by either hydrogen or gasoline [16]. At the beginning of the second fuel century, Ford has launched its P2000 concept model, and is developing a 6.8 L hydrogen piston engine for use in buses [17].

In the aviation world, on the other hand, hydrogen is being applied via the fuel cell (which is an **engine** and not a **fuel**!), currently to light aircraft and UAVs. AeroVironment, for example, is flying a third-scale model of its Global Observer aircraft powered by liquid hydrogen stored in a cryogenic tank [18], and has designed the Hornet micro flying wing utilising hydrogen, released from dry pellets when combined with water, fed to a 10 W fuel cell [19]. DynAero's Lafayette III light aircraft is to be fitted with two 30 kW fuel cells [20]. In the US, a team is working on highly efficient fuel cells fed with hydrogen derived from chemical combinations with atoms of lithium and aluminium, utilising nanoparticulate technology [21]. Also, the Lockheed Martin airship incorporates a plastic skin comprised of layers of an acidic polymer plus platinum catalysts and fine wire electrodes in the form of a 200 W fuel cell, fed from an internal supply of hydrogen from the reaction of lithium hydride with water [22]. Boeing's approach is to replace gas-turbine driven auxiliary power units in jet aircraft with fuel cells [23].

29

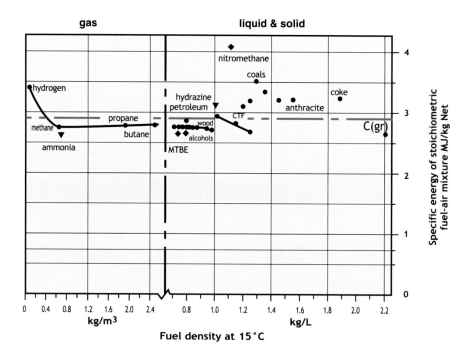

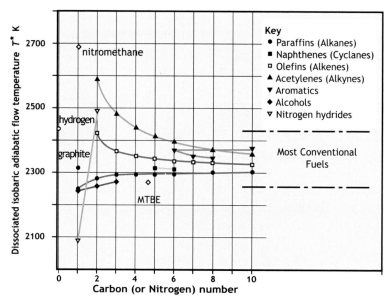

Figure 19
Specific energies of stoichiometric mixtures, and combustion temperatures showing relatively minor variations only.

In the rocketry sector, hydrogen is transferred routinely as a liquid over thousands of kilometres by means of tanker vehicles of about 40 000 L capacity that are super insulated with deep vacuum maintained by aluminium sheeting and glass felt, but larger quantities may be transferred as gas via a pipeline network, as in Europe.

Prediction No. 3 Hydrogen will find increasing use in aviation via the gas turbine, fuel cell and rocket, as the challenging problems of large-scale production and distribution become resolved, and will continue to provide thrust for travel in near space. It may prove commercially possible to generate hydrogen at airfields by electrolysis powered either by mains electricity or "green" sources of wind, hydroelectricity and solar as in the ITM Power [24] and Honda systems, or alternatively by extending the Honda home energy system using natural gas [25].

12. Advances in Fuel Testing Techniques

The comprehensive suite of tests for aviation fuels is continually under review by such bodies as the MoD's Aviation Fuels Committee and the Energy Institute in UK, the ASTM in US, and the test equipment manufacturers themselves. The significant improvements in convenience, speed and accuracy that have already emerged may be categorised as follows:

- Replacement of complex/expensive tests by empirical relationships with results from other, more convenient, tests, e.g. Specific energy (from H content), Distillation (from gas chromatography).

- Automatic operation of apparatus based on inbuilt computer, plus print-out of results,
  e.g. Freezing point, Flash point, Vapour pressure, Viscosity.

- Closer simulation of service conditions within test, e.g. Thermal stability.

- Rapid automatic chemical analysis followed by instant comparison against several hundred similar fuels, previously analysed and tested with results stored as references, plus minimal quantity of sample requirement (mL rather than L), e.g. Octane numbers [26].

Although all these developments are praiseworthy, the last-named has sparked the writer's imagination to the nth degree because, if a small chromatographic or other analyser can compare the sample against inbuilt data for a number of reference fuels within a period of about 8 seconds (cf. an hour or two for a CFR rating), why should this be restricted to octane number? This raises the heady prospect expressed in the following:

> **Prediction No. 4** Great strides will be made towards the holy grail of a magic black box into which a few mL of sample are injected via a hypodermic syringe and, after comparison with a large number of reference fuels, data on all the required properties are printed out within a few seconds!

13. Advanced Propulsion Systems

The following systems have been initiated in the first fuel century, and offer considerable promise in the second.

13.1 In Atmosphere

For advanced propulsion at modest levels of thrust, conversions to electrical drive are appearing, as shown:

2006   In UK, Autonomous Vehicles International has produced an electrically-powered dual ducted-fan UAV operating at 45 km/h with a ceiling of 600 m [27].

2007   In Italy, Galileo Avionica is developing the Asio electrically-powered VTOL UAV as a backpack unit [28].

> **Prediction No. 5** The concepts of more electric, and all electric, aircraft will flourish, the required on-board energy emanating from gas turbine combustion or nuclear reactions.

Near-space tourism is creating substantial interest from both potential aircraft suppliers, and their wealthy passenger applicants.

2004	Burt Rutan's SpaceShipOne won the Asari X-prize for putting a man in space, leading to Virgin Galactic's planning to offer the world's first commercial spaceflight in 2009 [**29**].
2007	EADS Astrium unveiled a novel concept comprising an all-composite fully-reusable spacecraft fitted with conventional turbojet engines, plus a liquid oxygen-methane rocket booster to carry a pilot and four passengers at Mach 3 to an altitude of 60 km, followed by coasting to 100 km. The trip would occupy 90 minutes, including 3 minutes of weightlessness, prior to a 4.5 g descent [**30**].

> **Prediction No. 6** By 2020, suborbital flights will be well established, with an estimated 5- to15-thousand thrill-seekers a year finding the £100 000, and the nerve, to participate.

The ongoing demand for higher flight speeds has promoted high-thrust engines such as scramjets and pulsed detonation tubes.

13.1.1 Ramjets and Scramjets

In the conventional ramjet, the level of pressure required for efficient combustion is achieved by diffusion in the entry section as the air is decelerated to about Mach 0.2 to facilitate flame stabilisation, whereas in the supersonic combustion ramjet, fuels of a relatively high flame speed, such as hydrogen, are attractive although hydrocarbons are being used successfully. Advanced ramjets include those heated by highly energetic non-chemical sources. The following are representative of developments that have occurred at the beginning of this second fuel century:

2003	USAF examined the feasibility of powering a UAV with a quantum nucleonic reactor in which X-rays lower the energy levels of certain isomeric particles of radioactive hafnium-178. the resulting energy (60 times that supplied) appearing as gamma rays that are arranged to heat the air stream [**31**].
2004	NASA launched the HYPER-X based on a pilotless hypersonic scramjet-powered vehicle from a Boeing B52 bomber above the Pacific Ocean, the 1.3 ton vehicle reaching Mach 9.65. Hydrogen fuel was used, with silane (SiH_4) - hypergolic with air - as an igniter [**32**]. Pratt &Whitney devised jointly with Boeing a scramjet programme for a Mach 6-7 waverider using JP-7 for both combustion and cooling [**33**]. The AFRL planned a scramjet based on JP-7, ignited by either ethene (ethylene) or high-temperature gas to replace silane which generates solid products [**34**].
2005	In Italy, a Mach 2 scramjet study concluded that combustion occurs with volume, rather than pressure, constant, and that hydrogen fuel is optimal since combustion lasts for one millisecond only [**35**].

2006	Pratt & Whitney completed ground tests on the GDE-2 scramjet at Mach 5 using JP-7, with ethene for ignition [36]. In Australia, QinetiQ's HYSHOT III scramjet vehicle operating with hydrogen was launched, and has led to the more promising HYCAUSE vehicle, due shortly for testing [37].

13.1.2 Pulsed Detonation Propulsers

The application of the pulse-detonation constant-volume cycle to jet propulsion is estimated to reduce the specific fuel consumption by 5 to 10%.   Other benefits include low-cost operation, almost instant acceleration/deceleration, and few moving parts. Noise is one of the key challenges, but this is dampened if a gas-turbine engine is fitted downstream as part of a hybrid package.

2003	Pratt & Whitney tested a 5-tube 60 Hz engine supplied with pressurised air to simulate Mach 2.5, operating on ethene, oxygen and compressed air [38]. The AFRL planned the flight of a 4-tube engine to generate up to 0.89 kN thrust at 20 Hz [37].
2004	The FAA issued an airworthiness certificate for a Rutan LongEZ aircraft powered by an experimental detonation engine developed by AFRL, designed for Mach 4 [40]. A consortium of GE, Pratt & Whitney and Rolls-Royce is researching a multi-tube rotating engine comparable to a revolver, using Jet A, propane and ethene, but flight speeds in excess of Mach 4 may be achieved using hydrogen [41].
2005	The AFRL project was improved. US interest centres on applications to supersonic and hypersonic missiles, replacement of afterburners in combat aircraft, and unmanned aircraft [42].

13.2 In Deep Space

To provide any significant propulsive performance in deep space, the limitations of vehiclar capacity in terms of both mass and volume will, with certain exceptions. demand the ultra-high energy output of a nuclear source.   One fundamental advantage of such an approach is that the type and properties of the energy source (the reactants) may be entirely independent from those of the propelling fluid (the propellant).   This raises the possibilities of optimising both materials separately, in contrast to chemical rocketry.   For very long-term voyages within deep space (e.g. beyond Mars), on the other hand, modest levels of thrust dependent on solar radiation alone may be acceptable.

The following systems apply, with representative schematic designs shown in Fig. 20.

13.2.1 Nuclear

(a) Heat Transfer Fission Rocket.   Propellant flows through channels in a nuclear reactor, controlled by insertion of moderating rods, giving twice the specific impulse of chemical rockets.   Radioisotope thermoelectric generators are also possible.

2003	One of the propulsive systems developed by NASA for Project Prometheus to probe the icy crust of the Europa moon of Jupiter is based on the nuclear heat transfer fission rocket. Both uranium 235 and plutonium 238 are considered as fuel sources, with hydrogen as propellant [43].

Nuclear

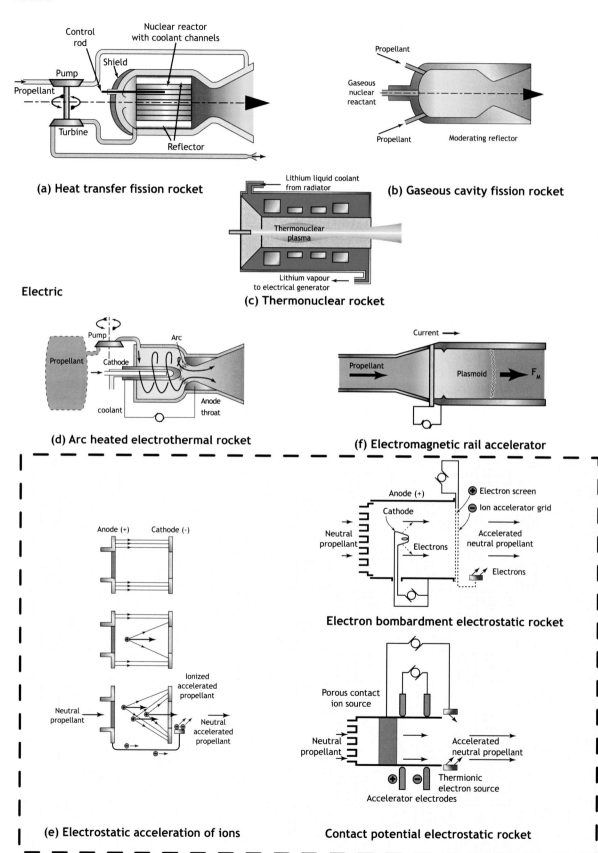

(a) Heat transfer fission rocket

(b) Gaseous cavity fission rocket

(c) Thermonuclear rocket

Electric

(d) Arc heated electrothermal rocket

(f) Electromagnetic rail accelerator

Electron bombardment electrostatic rocket

(e) Electrostatic acceleration of ions

Contact potential electrostatic rocket

Figure 20
Schematics of propulsion systems for deep space.

(b) Gaseous Cavity Fission Rocket.   Propellant mixed with gaseous nuclear reactant in the chamber prior to ejection, but emissions are radioactive.

(c) Thermonuclear Rocket.   Control of fusion plasma by pinch effect, but initiation difficult.

2003   NASA is developing a nuclear-fusion engine to generate 300 times the thrust of a chemical rocket, based on on-board fusion by a mixture of deuterium and tritium to 100 million kelvin, cutting the Earth-Mars journey time from 6 months to 6 weeks [44]!

Prediction No. 7   The Orion project (1965), in which a spacecraft fitted with a pusher plate is propelled by repeated nuclear explosions behind it, will not be reinstated because of the ban on nuclear explosions in space, but nuclear fission and fusion propulsion will receive further study.

13.2.2   Electric

(d) Electrothermal.   Heat addition to propellant effected electrically by either arc (Arcjet) or heat exchanger (Resistojet).

(e) Electrostatic.   Propellant ionised at anode, the electrons being removed and used to neutralise the ions after acceleration through the cathode.

2003   The Safe Affordable Fission Engine (SAFE) is designed to use about 100 kg of uranium 235 to produce 100 kW of electricity to strip electrons off atoms of xenon, and accelerate the positively-charged ions [43]. NASA also completed an endurance test of its xenon ion thruster for long-term wear [45]. In Europe, an ion thruster is scheduled to provide the main propulsion to ESA's Artemis satellite to correct its orbit [46].

2004   NASA completed initial tests of the 12 kW HiPEP engine utilsing xenon ionised by microwaves [47].

2005   In Japan, the Muses-C xenon-propelled spacecraft has logged over 20 000 hours in visiting asteroid 1998 SF36 [48]. In Europe, the Smart-1 lunar probe has exhausted its xenon propellant [49].

2006   In Europe, the ESA and Australian National University jointly tested an ion engine for a Mars vehicle.   Double grids with a voltage disparity prevent collision damage [50].

(f) Electromagnetic.   Propellant plasmoid generated between electrode rails, then accelerated to exit, being replaced immediately on a pulsed basis.

13.2.3   Solar

The solar energy permeating space can be utilised to propel a vehicle either indirectly by solar-cell electric propulsion, or directly by a solar sail.

Solar Cells

A combination of solar cells and storage batteries permits continuous flight through day- and night-time hours.

2003 The unmanned NASA/AeroVironment 75 m span Helios flying wing that had emerged with such promise in 2001 unfortunately crashed into the Pacific Ocean following self- induced oscillation due to failure of the flight control system [51]. The National Aerospace Laboratory in Japan successfully flew a 47 m long unmanned airship into the stratosphere. At least 20 more craft are planned to operate for flights up to 10 years at 20 km altitude powered by solar energy [52]. In Switzerland, Dr Bertrand Piccard is planning to circumnavigate the globe in 2010 using the Solar Impulse aircraft [53].

2004 In US, the Los Alamos National Laboratory is able to increase the output of solar cells by 35% using semiconductor nanocrystals [54].

2005 AC Propulsion flew a 4.75 m SoLong solar-electric drone for a period exceeding 24 hours [55].

2006 NASA and Ad Astra Rocket Co. are collaborating on the Variable Specific Impulse Magnetoplasma Rocket (Vasimr), incorporating solar panels, for interplanetary travel, with hydrogen as the initial propellant [56].

Solar sail

Although the thrust of a solar sail is small, it is constant so that acceleration is continuous, and speeds may eventually exceed 600 000 km/h.

2004 In Japan, two 7.5 micrometre thin-film configurations have been deployed at altitudes up to 169 km [57].

2005 NASA tested a solar sail deployment system using inflatable aluminised material with a coiled graphite boom that can be uncoiled remotely [58].

2006 The University of California designed a giant flexible solar-electric membrane to supply an array of xenon ion engines to provide propulsion and impart tautness, intended to propel a 200 kg space probe to Pluto within less than a year [59].

The major propellant requirements are listed in Fig. 21 Note that our initial concern with aerospace fuels now encompasses oxidants and, ultimately, propellants.

Prediction No. 8 High-speed flight within the atmosphere will make increasing use of scramjets and pulsed detonation units, whereas ionic propulsion together with nuclear and electric systems are likely to be adopted for space.

POTENTIAL FUELS FOR SECOND CENTURY OF AEROSPACE

Altitude	Mach	Propulsive System	Fuel Feature	Potential Fuels
A				
Subsonic				
Moderate<1		Gas turbine	Supply	Petroleum Avtur (to 2050+)
		"	"	Supplemental Avtur
		Fuel cell/motor	High Electrochem	Hydrogen
		Solar cell/motor	Continuous	Solar radiation
B				
Supersonic				
High	2	Gas turbines	High Th. Stability	Paraffinic JPTS
	3	"	Low Sp.Ignitability	Cyclic & isomer molecules
	3	GT/Ramjets	High ED	Dense hcs/Non C hydrides/slurries
	4	Ramjets	High Th. Capacity	High T. Cyclics & Dimers
		Pulsed burners	High Sp. Ignitability	?
Hypersonic				
High	5	Ramjets	High Th. Capacity	Vaporising Cyclics & Dimers
	8	"	"	Thermal Endothermic " " "
	10	Scramjets	"	Catalytic " " " "
			"	Cryogens, LH$_2$ or LCH$_4$
			[Propellant Feature, and Potentials]	
	20	"	Low M$_p$ Combn. products	} LH$_2$ to H$_2$O (M$_p$ = 18)
			& High Combn.Temp.	} cf. C to CO$_2$ (M$_p$= 44)
	Variable	Rockets		} Hydrogen
C				
Space				

Electrothermal	} [Ease of ionisation, hence high M$_p$]
Electrostatic	
Electromagnetic	
Electrothermoacoustic	Helium
Gaseous cavity fission	[Low M$_p$, low thermal neutron absorption]
Thermonuclear	[Low M$_p$, high thermal neuton absorption]
Nuclear particle emitter	
Photon	
Microwaves (ground based)	Hydrogen
Solar heater	Xenon
Solar sails	solar radiation
Antimatter	

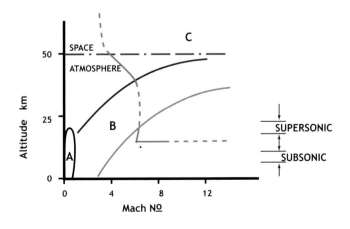

Figure 21

13.2.4 Antimatter

Other systems of space propulsion include thermoacoustic, ground-based microwaves, photons and ground-based lasers to either promote ablation of vehicle material, or energise photovoltaic cells mounted on the underside. However, the ultimate in rocket propulsion energy is represented by mass-energy conversion via antimatter.

Protons and antiprotons are examples of the concept that every subatomic particle has an associated antiparticle exhibiting opposite properties. Annihilation of these materials can then be controlled to give pions and other charged particles, the energy released being applied in a variety of ways:

- catalyse microfission, yielding a specific impulse of 135 kN s/kg (cf. 4 by chemical means)

- initiate microfission/fusion, yielding 610 kN s/kg, or

- direct annihilation in beamed core engine, yielding 10 000 kN s/kg.

The products could be flow-controlled magnetically to produce thrust, giving the capability of reaching Mars in 30 days, and permitting exploration of the galaxy within a human lifetime.

2004   Despite the extreme difficulty in containment of antiprotons, Penn State University has managed to build a trap to hold them for a period of 18 days [60].

Prediction No. 9 Significant steps are likely to be made towards the production, retention and annihilation of antimatter, vastly increasing the potential of galaxy exploration.

Prediction No. 10 The second aerospace fuel year is likely to prove even more exciting than the first, with much extended space tourism, solar sail races to the Moon, and ever-increasing exploration of distant astronomical targets.

14. Collated Predictions

No. 1   Aviation kerosine will remain largely petroleum-based for about 40 years, but supplies will continue to be supplemented progressively from natural gas, coal, the large deposits of shale oil and tar, and perpetually-available biomatter. Algae appear particularly promising, and wild grasses perhaps even more so, whereas genetic engineering may permit the design of a perfect crop for a fuel source, with the needs for cultivation space eased by partial terraforming of the desert using seawater, combined with aerial re-vegetation by dropping seedlings in liquid-filled containers.

No. 2   Vegetable-based alcohols, possibly produced via solar energy, will endure for light piston-engined aircraft, including UAVs, and for some less intensive rockets, but will not apply to main gas turbine engines.

No. 3   Hydrogen will find increasing use in aviation via the gas turbine, fuel cell and rocket, as the challenging problems of large-scale production and distribution become resolved, and will continue to provide thrust for travel in near space. It may prove commercially possible to generate hydrogen at airfields by electrolysis powered either by mains electricity or "green" sources of wind, hydroelectricity and solar as in the ITM Power [24] and Honda systems, or alternatively by extending the Honda home energy system using natural gas [25]

No. 4 Great strides will be made towards the holy grail of a magic black box into which a few mL of sample are injected via a hypodermic syringe and, after comparison with a large number of reference fuels, data on all the required properties are printed out within a few seconds!

No. 5 The concepts of more electric, and all electric, aircraft will flourish, the required on-board energy emanating from gas turbine combustion or nuclear reactions.

No. 6 By 2020, suborbital flights will be well established, with an estimated 5- to 15-thousand thrill-seekers a year finding the £100 000, and the nerve, to participate.

No. 7 The Orion project (1965), in which a spacecraft fitted with a pusher plate is propelled by repeated nuclear explosions behind it, will not be reinstated because of the ban on nuclear explosions in space, but nuclear fission and fusion propulsion will receive further study.

No. 8 High-speed flight within the atmosphere will make increasing use of scramjets and pulsed detonation units, whereas ionic propulsion together with nuclear and electric systems are likely to be adopted for space.

No. 9 Significant steps are likely to be made towards the production, retention and annihilation of antimatter, vastly increasing the potential of galaxy exploration.

No. 10 The second aerospace fuel year is likely to prove even more exciting than the first, with space diving, much extended space tourism, solar sail races to the Moon, and ever-increasing exploration of distant astronomical targets.

15. Note on Emissions

The highly topical issue of aviation emissions is crucial, but since it requires specialist knowledge, this writer prefers to restrict his own comments to the following --

- This is a complex issue, but current misconceptions regarding the climatic impact of aviation must be countered.

- Agreement should be reached on whether or not man's production of CO_2 is the main driver of climate change.

- With problems of CO_2, low specific energy, flame radiation and potentially of CO, unburnt hydrocarbons, aldehydes, soot and smoke, there seems to be no alternative but to eliminate carbon from future fuels.

- With hydrogen cryoplanes, the acute problem of the climatic impact of contrails may be eased by the larger mean effective size of the particles involved.

-- and then seek further advice from the experts in this field.

Anyone for space?   Only £99,999.99 a throw!
Terms and conditions apply

Appendix 1. Nomenclature

A) Hydrocarbons

Series Name		Description	General Molecular Formula	Main Characteristics
Fuel Technology	Organic Chemistry			
Paraffins	Alkanes	Open-chain saturated	C_nH_{2n+2}	Storage stability High H → high SE
Olefins	Alkenes	Open-chain unsaturated Double bonded	C_nH_{2n}	Storage instability
Naphthenes	Cyclanes	Closed-chain saturated	$(CH_2)_n$	Storage stability
Acetylenes	Alkynes	Open-chain unsaturated Triple bonded	C_nH_{2n-2}	**Highly unstable** Optimal combn. temp., flame speed & flamm. range
Aromatics	Aromatics	Closed-chain unsaturated Resonance bonded	C_nH_{2n-6} etc.	Attacks seals & diaphragms High C → Smoke & low SE

n = carbon number   H is monovalent   C is tetravalent

B) Recommendations

Gasoline rather than Petrol

Kerosine rather than Kerosene

Density (units kg/L at specified temperature, e.g 15°C) rather than non-dimensional Specific Gravity, or Relative Density

Spark Knock rather than Detonation

Specific Energy rather than Gravimetric Calorific Value

Energy Density rather than Volumetric Calorific Value

Calorific Values to include both Specific Energy and Energy Density, only net values being meaningful

Molar Mass rather than Atomic Weight, or Molecular Weight

Biomatter (when no mass is stated) rather than Biomass

Flammable rather than Inflammable

Cleanness (representing condition) rather than Cleanliness (representing behaviour)

SI units wherever possible

Litre represented by upper-case 'L' since lower-case 'l' can be confused with figure one.

Appendix 2.   Fuel Consumption, Mtonnes

A)   Transport Fuels in UK

Fuel	1993 (%)		2006 (%)		% Change from 2005
Avgas	**0.027**	**(0.03)**	**0.04**	**(0.05)**	**(-21.68)**
Mogas	23.77	(28.26)	18.67	(22.49)	(2.10)
Avtur	**7.11**	**(8.45)**	**14.18**	**(17.08)**	**(2.64)**
Derv	11.81	(14.04)	21.39	(25.77)	(7.97)
Diesel	7.78	(9.25)	6.16	(7.42)	(-6.21)
Total UK	84.1	(100)	83.0	(100)	(-1.00)
Total World	3132		3890		(0.7)

Appendix 3. Cutting the Aviation Fuel Bill

About 85 000 flights take off each day, consuming over 50 billion US gallons annually, possibly doubling by 2050. Coupled with the rising prices of oil, proposals to constrain the aviation fuel bill (in addition to continuing improvements in engine and aerodynamic efficiencies) include the following:

- Carry return fuel on the outward journey when costs are lower at the departure point.

- Bottle in-flight duty-free alcohol in plastic rather than glass.

- Reduce the fuel load by an amount proportional to the number of child passengers.

- Add winglets to reduce drag.

- Taxi on a single engine only.

- Ensure routes are as direct as possible.

- Limit the use of auxiliary power units on the ground.

- Distribute passengers to achieve a fuel-efficient centre of gravity.

- Not load an aircraft with more than the prescribed amount of fuel.

- Find closer emergency landing airports in order to reduce flight-fuel reserves from 10 to 5% [61].

Additional proposals include:

- Adopt the Domestic Reduced Vertical Separation Minimum from 0.6 to 0.3 km,

- Avoid altitudes of supersaturated air.

- Improve air traffic management at departures and arrivals, plus new flight planning systems.

- Adopt lighter more-electric aircraft.

- Develop engine technologies to optimise performance across the complete flight envelope.

- Split long journeys into legs of, say, 5000 km each.

- Refuel civil aircraft in-flight [62].

Also:

- Flap setting adjustment at take-off and landing.

- Reduction in cruising speeds to Mach 0.8.

- Water washing of engines on wing.

- Distribution of reading materials to passengers prior to boarding so that unused material is left in the airport [63].

Notes: Fuel efficiency of modern aircraft is reported as 3.5 L/100 pax km (<3 for 787 and A380).

The fuel bill for airlines will rise to $117 billion in 2007 [64] representing 26% of direct operating costs [65].

Representative specification limits (mean properties) of conventional & alternative aerospace fuels

Property	Avgas	Avtag JP-4	Avtur JP-8	Avcat JP-5	Gas oil	JPTS	JP-7	JP-10	RP-1	RJ-1	Methanol	Ethanol	Methane	Hydrogen
Formula	$(C_{7.3}H_{15.3})$		$(C_{12.5}H_{24.4})$						$(C_{12.5}H_{24.6})$		CH_3OH	C_2H_5OH	CH_4	H_2
M g/mol	(102.,9)		(174.4)						(174.6)		32.042	46.068	16.043	2.016
C % mass	(85.1)		(86.0)		86.5	86.0	85.6		(85.9)		37.5	52.1	74.8	0
Density (g) kg/m³													0.679	0.085
Density (l) kg/L	Report (0.72)	0.751-0.802	0.775-0840	0.788-0.845	0.820-0.845	0.767-0.797	0.779-0.806	0.935-0.943	0.800-0.815	0.842-0.863	0.792	0.789	0.415*	0.072*
bp °C	Report (40)-170	Report-270	Report (150)-300 (260)	Report-300	(165-)350	157-260	182-288		180-263	221-315	64.8	78.4	-161.5	-252.7
fp °C	-58	-58	-47(-53)	-46	-7	-53	-43.3	-79	-48	-40	-95.5	-117.3	-184.0	-259.1
Flamm limits % vol. in air	(1-6)	(1-5.5)	(1-5)	(1-4)	(1-4)						6-36	4-19	5-15	4-75
Flash pt °C	-	-	38(42)	61	55(68)	43	60	54.4	57		11	57	-	-
Net Sp Energy MJ/kg	43.5	42.8(43.5)	42.8(43.3)	42.6	(42.5)	42.8	43.5	42.1	43.5	43.0	19.9	26.8	50.1	120.2
Net En Density (g) MJ/m³													33.98	10.22
Net En Density (l) MJ/L	(31.3)	(33.9)	(34.7)	(34.9)	(35.7)	(33.4)	(34.4)	(39.6)	(35.2)	(36.6)	15.8	21.1	20.8	8.59

* At boiling point

References

1. N Beheshti & A C McIntosh, A biomimetric study of the explosive discharge of the bombardier beetle, Int. Journal of Design & Nature, vol. 1, No. 1, 2007, pp 61-69

2. Air transport, Boeing selects supplier for 7E7 tank inerting, Flight International, 6-12 July 2004, p 9

3. G Warwick, Eclipse makes fire safety lap, Flight International, 2-8 August 2005, p 25

4. M Pliskin, Fuel renewal, Flight International, 3-9 October 2006, p 30

5. J Ott, Synthetics soar, Aviation Week & Space Technology, 31 July 2006, p 54

6. P Expedito, Biofuels from vegetable and animal oils as methyl or ethyl esters, Tebio, Brazil

7. China eyes green fuel, Flight International, 23-29 August 2005, p 15

8. J Cunningham, The sky's the limit, Professional Engineering, 25 January 2006, p 28

9. News Break, Aviation Week & Space Technology, 18-25 December 2006, p 14

10. J Cunningham, Biofuels join the jet set, Professional Engineering, 23 May 2007,, p 32

11. Growing algae could cut the cost of producing biodiesel, Professional Engineering, 9 May 2007, p 45

12. C S Smith, A French wine of character that may wind up in a gas tank, New York Times via The Daily Telegraph, 13 October 2005

13. Ethanol Ipanema, Flight International, 30 November-6 December 2004, p 26

14. P Eisenstein, Ground force, Professional Engineering, 14 June 2006, p 45

15. Hydro car is top of the track, Professional Engineering, 6 October 2004, p 11

16. Mazda's renosed Renesis makes case for dual-fuel, Professional Engineering, 5 November 2003, p 8

17. New hydrogen cars fuelling stations in the US, Energy World, October 2001, p 6

18. M A Dornheim, Fuel-cell flier, Aviation Week & Space Technology, 27 June 2005, p 52

19. Hornet is fuel-cell first, Flight International, 13-19 May 2003, p 38

20. G Norris, ATP plans to fly electrically-powered light aircraft early in 2004, Flight International, 5-11 August 2003, p 30

21. P J Parmalee, For UAVs too, Aviation Week & Space Technology, 24 October 2005, p 14

22. J Marchant, Pushing the envelope, NewScientist, 3 March 2001, p 20

23. R Coppinger, Green light, Flight International, 23-29 August 2005, p 36

24. Smart homes develop their own power, Professional Engineering, 19 September 2007, p 47

25. Dream, Honda customer magazine, 2007, p 30 (dream@honda-eu.com)

26. D Brown, Octane determination using light and mirrors?, Petroleum Review, June 1994, p 281

27 UK ducted-fan UAV unveiled, Flight International, 8-14 August 2006, p 27

28 Galileo takes to the skies with Asio electrically powered UAV, Flight International, 20-26 February 2007, p 20

29. http://www.virgingalactic.com .

30. J Cunningham, Holidays in orbit, Professional Engineering, 11 July 2007, p 39

31. US Air Force plans nuclear drones, NewScientist, 22 Febrary 2003, p 4

32. G Norris, Last gasp?, Flight International, 23-29 November 2004, p ,47

33. G Warwick, USAF kick starts scramjet tests, Flight International, 27 January-2 February 2004, p 24

34. S W Kandebo, Bigger may be better, Aviation Week & Space Technology, 16 August 2004, p 50

35. Scramjet modelling tools 'must change', Flight International, 5-11 July 2005, p 30

36. G Warwick, Mach 5 scramjet tunnel test paves way for X-51A, Flight International, 11-17 July 2006, p 44

37. G Warwick, HyCause ramjet ready for flight, Flight International, 8-14 May 2007, p 26

38. G Norris, Pulse detonation engine moves closer to reality, Flight International, 25-31 March 2003, p 28

39. G Norris, Pulse detonation engine set to fly, Flight International, 29 July-4 August 2003, p 5

40. S W Kandebo, Flights of fancy, Aviation Week & Space Technology, 8 March 2004, p30

41. S W Kandebo, Taking the pulse, Aviation Week & Space Technology, 8 March 2004, p 32.

42. G Norris, Pulse detonation trials back on, Flight International, 26 July-1 August 2005, p 28

43. K Kleiner, Fission control, NewScientist, 12 April 2003, p 39

44. D Grahame-Rowe, Earth to Mars in just six weeks, NewScientist, 25 January 2003, p 23

45. NASA trial multiplies ion thruster's life by four, Flight International, 12-18 August 2003, p 26

46. Rocket science, NewScientist, 1 February 2003, p 7

47. Microwaves mean longer life for ion propulsion, Flight International, 2-8 December 2003, p 42

48. F Morring Jr, Building time, Aviation Week & Space Technology, 31 January 2005, p 18

49. F Morring Jr, Smart-1 shutdown, Aviation Week & Space Technology, 26 September 2005, p 17

50. Ion engine could fly to Mars, Flight International, 24-30 January 2006, p 30

51. G Norris, Helios board looks at cause of 'severe oscillations', Flight International, 15-21 July 2003, p 26

52. M Fitzpatrick, Japan's blimp flies high, NewScientist, 16 August 2003, p 7

53. Fly by the Sun, Professional Engineering, 10 December 2003

54. P J Parmalee, More power, Aviation Week & Space Technology, 10 May 2004, p 13

55. Aviation Week & Space Technology, 13 June 2005, p 30

56. R Coppinger, NASA spins out gridless plasma rocket design, Flight International, 21-27 February 2006, p 36

57. F Morring Jr, Solar sail, Aviation Week & Space Technology, 16 August 2004, p 19

58. F Morring Jr, Sailing on sunbeams, Aviation Week & Space Technology, 25 April 2005, p 17

59. P Marks, Will a flying carpet take us to Pluto?, NewScientist, 29 April 2006, p 28

60. http://www.engr.psu.edu/antimatter

61. J C Ansemo, Desperate measures, Aviation Week & Space Technology, 6 December 2004, p 54

62. J Jupp, Impact of Aviation on the Environment, The Aerospace Professional, August 2007, p 9

63. R Wall, TAP-ping savings, Aviation Week & Space Technology, 8 May 2006, p 41

64. G Bisignani, We are misunderstood, and it's our own fault, Aviation Week & Space Technology, 16 April, 2007, p 86

65. P Sparaco, Synthetic solution, Aviation Week & Space Technology, 16 October 2006, p 71

INDEX

Transport Fuels Technology

ISBN 0 9520186 2 4
444 pages, 8 chapters,
58 appendices,
over 200 figures (*many coloured*),
63 tables, bibliographies
Soft cover,
Medium Quarto, (235 x 276 mm) x 25mm.

LANDFALL PRESS

Published by Landfall
Press, Norwich,
supported by the
Energy Institute , 2000

£40

(+ £8 p&p beyond Europe)

ORDER FROM PORTLAND PRESS,
Customer Services:
sales@portlandpress.com,
or via The Energy Institute's publication
website:
www.energyinstpubs.org.uk

Transport is vital for today's lifestyles.
Speed and reliability demand powered propulsion, and hence suitable fuels.
Preliminary reviews cover hydrocarbon chemistry, engineering thermodynamics, and combustion principles. These are followed by in-depth discussions of the sources, types, production, properties, testing, handling, combustion performance and emissions of both conventional and alternative fuels plus rocket reactants. The book concludes with a reasoned assessment of transport prospects for the future.
Essential source material for scientists and engineers interested in transport fuel science and technology, as well as librarians, information scientists, managers and planners

Transport Fuels Technology has four hundred and forty four pages, comprising eight chapters each with an individual chapter index cross referenced to other chapters, and a comprehensive bibliography. There are fifty eight appendices, over two hundred detailed figures, many coloured, and sixty three tables. Each chapter is colour coded for easy reference, and margin notes highlighting relevant points guide the reader to a more in-depth explanation.

Sample pages show standard of detail and layout

Illustrations of Skycar reproduced by kind permission of Moller

---

Transport Fuels Technology

QUARTERLY UPDATE SERVICE

The author of Transport Fuels Technology updates with news of developments in the transport fuels sector from year 2000 by preparing abstracts of carefully-selected worldwide literature, including technical journals, conference proceedings, special reports, books and databases.

Over 1200 abstracts to date are published on the Energy Institute's website, accessible to subscribers via a customer password or by email delivery to their desktop. The abstracts are arranged under 24 headings within 5 groups:

1. SURFACE TRANSPORT

Gasolines
Diesel fuels
Compressed natural gas
Liquefied natural gas
Liquefied petroleum gases
Methanol
Biodiesel
Bioethanol & other oxygenates
Hydrogen

2. AEROSPACE

Aero piston engines
Thermal stability
Freezing
Aero general

3. FUEL HANDLING

Fire safety
Contamination
Volatility

4. PROPULSION

Auto heat engines
Battery-electric vehicles
Hybrid vehicles
Fuel cell vehicles
Solar propulsion
Novel propulsive systems

5. GENERAL

Fuel consumption & emissions
Fuel synthesis

Included are correlated booklets for periods 2000 to 2004, 2005 and 2006 available as a free pdf to all subscribers.
A comprehensive index is also provided online for Transport Fuels Technology.
Annual Subscription Rate for 4 issues
Non members of EI: *£125.00*
Members of EI: *£95.00*
Order via email: lis@energyinst.org.uk